IMAGES OF WALES

SOUTH WALES COLLIERIES

VOLUME SIX

MINING DISASTERS

The Price of Coal

Pit sheaves, winder, drams of coal,
Hunger marches, picket lines, strikes and dole,
Davy lamps shining, saviours of brass,
Explosions, flooding, methane gas,
Hob nailed boots, cage, hooter's call,
Sudden disasters and many a 'fall',
Water jack, bacco, snuff, Tommy box,
Under an arm, a bundle of blocks,
Mandrills, winches, rings of steel,
Pit ponies, coal cutters and big wheel,
Snaking 'journeys', pit props, pumps
Clearing water from the sumps,
Gasping, wheezing silicosis,
Killer pneumoconiosis,
Sudsy tin baths, twice used water,
Black backs washed by mam or daughter,
Dai-capped, mufflered, blue-scarred men,
Ianto, Glyndwr, Jack and Ben,
Jokes, camaraderie, cheerful grin,
Butties, comrades through thick and thin.

For sacrifices miners made
Never can that debt be paid,
Pain and anguish, grime and sweat,
Hardships no one should forget.

By Hawys Glyn James

Comfort and Promises

Another leaf has fallen,
Another soul has gone
But still we have God's promises
In every robin's song;
For He is in His Heaven
And though He takes away
He always leaves to mortals
The bright sun's kindly ray.
He leaves the fragrant blossoms
And Lovely forests, green,
And gives us new found comfort
When we on Him will lean.

Author unknown

IMAGES OF WALES

SOUTH WALES COLLIERIES

VOLUME SIX

MINING DISASTERS

DAVID OWEN

The History Press

First published in 2005 by Tempus Publishing

Reprinted in 2010 by
The History Press
The Mill, Brimscombe Port,
Stroud, Gloucestershire, GL5 2QG
www.thehistorypress.co.uk

Reprinted 2011

British Library Cataloguing in Publication Data.
A catalogue record for this book is available from the British Library.

ISBN 978 0 7524 3564 0

Typesetting and origination by Tempus Publishing Limited.
Printed and bound in Great Britain by
Marston Book Services Limited, Didcot

Contents

Acknowledgements

Man searches the farthest recesses for ore in the blackest darkness. Near where people dwell he cuts a shaft. No bird of prey knows that hidden path. Proud beasts do not set foot on it. Man tunnels through the rock; his eyes see all its treasures. He brings hidden Golden Nuggets of Coal to light. Neither gold nor crystal can compare with it nor can it be had for jewels or gold. Coral and jasper are not worthy of mention; the price of Coal is beyond rubies. The topaz of Cush cannot compare with it; it can only be bought with pure gold. It is hidden from the eyes of living things. It leads to Disasters, Accidents and Untold Misery.

Despite being among the most prolific in the British Coalfield, the South Wales Coalfield proved to be extremely difficult and dangerous to mine. Every few years an explosion occurred of such magnitude as to bring home to the public the risks run by miners. The list of colliery disasters caused by explosions is interesting reading; but it was these disasters rather than the daily tale of killed and injured which resulted in Parliament taking steps to introduce safety measures in the mines.

The Disasters, Accidents and Untold Misery to men, boys and pit ponies in this book are an everlasting tribute to the brave miners who gave their lives for the Golden Nuggets of Coal. I dedicate my book to the people of South Wales, the Land of Song, and to the memory of all the miners who worked at the collieries.

I sincerely thank everyone for their kindness and help.

David Owen
Author and Archivist

Preface

Black Gold – Aur Du, the Tragedies of Disasters, Accidents and Untold Misery in the South Wales Coalfield.

This great coalfield is assumed by various authorities to be approximately 1,000 square miles, which are distributed as follows: Glamorganshire 518 square miles, Breconshire 74 square miles, Carmarthenshire 228 square miles, Pembrokeshire 76 square miles and Monmouthshire 104 square miles. Of the above, nearly 846 square miles are exposed, about 153 square miles lie beneath the sea and about one square mile is covered by newer formations.

We continue our journey with *South Wales Collieries Volume Six: Mining Disasters*. Mining disasters and accidents have woven a dark pattern of tragedy throughout the history of coal mining, which has always been one of the more dangerous trades. Roman poets and the earliest English poetry have told of the perils of the sea. But have they amounted to so much more in loss of life and bodies maimed than the perils of the mine? For many years more accidents were reported in mines than in all the factories and workshops of the United Kingdom. Despite being among the most prolific in the country, the South Wales pits proved to be extremely difficult to mine. The deep seams, which provided the highly prized steam coal, were both gaseous and fiery, and as a consequence work was hard and always fraught with danger. All too often explosions, roof falls and other everyday accidents resulted in crippling injuries or death. Industrial diseases like pneumoconiosis caused near suffocation and almost inevitably proved fatal. The families of the miners lived at all times under the shadow of calamity, great or small.

The rapid growth of the South Wales Coalfield brought untold misery to thousands whose living depended upon it. Yet almost as nocuous were the effects of strikes and lockouts which occurred with alarming regularity. During the early part of the last century welfare payments did not exist so that any prolonged period of unemployment resulted in real hardship. Often during these times the basic necessities, however meagre, were usually only obtainable on credit, which was repayable once back at work. After a prolonged period of unemployment miners were often forced to obtain further credit in order to pay off the original arrears. Thus whole communities were caught in a never-ending spiral of debt.

It is well known that borers working on hard headings developed silicosis. In a heading near Aberdare, which eleven men were set to drive, as the money was good, many of them worked double shifts. Before the heading was driven through, ten of the men had to give up work, and later died of silicosis. A further hazard was from nystagmus, an eye disorder contracted through working in low light levels. Cases of this increased with the introduction of the safety lamp with its poor illumination qualities. The condition not only caused blindness but when left untreated could cause insanity. It is no exaggeration to say that those who worked below ground became old before their time.

David Owen
Author and Archivist

Foreword

It gives me great pleasure to write the foreword to this, David Owen's eleventh book, this time covering accidents and disasters and the latest in a series of books on the South Wales Collieries.

I left school on a Friday afternoon and I started work at Bargoed Colliery, Galleries Training Centre, Bargoed in the Rhymney Valley on the following Monday morning for my supervision and training as a miner. I worked underground doing various tasks at Groesfaen Colliery, near Deri in the Darran Valley, Ogilvie Colliery, near Deri in the Darran Valley, Markham Colliery, Markham in the Sirhowy Valley and Penallta Colliery, Hengoed in the Rhymney Valley. I worked on night preparation and maintenance at Markham and I also worked on developing the old roadway from Markham Colliery to Oakdale Colliery.

I was carrying a 4in steel pipe along the underground main roadway at Markham when the pipes above me collapsed and fell on top of me; consequently I suffered a fractured leg. When Markham closed in 1985 I was transferred to Penallta Colliery, but the colliery doctor retired me on ill health because of the injury I had received on my leg and unfortunately this was the end of my mining career and my working life.

My mining memories are etched on the pages of my mind and in the pages of this book by David; they are a fitting tribute to all the miners who worked at the collieries and will bring a fresh insight into an important time in our history that will revive the interest of young and old alike.

'The good old days', that is what they say, but there was so much poverty, pain and heartache during those good old days. We cannot ignore our history, but nor can we live in the past. We may study the past not to indulge our nostalgia for a bygone era but, rather, that we might learn lessons from it.

There has been so much pain and suffering. There were so many accidents and disasters in the pits and so many killed: 1897–930; 1898–908; 1899–916; 1900–1,012; 1901–1,101; 1903–1,072, 1904–1,049. The list goes on and on. Nor does this complete the tale; for every death there were several maimings. In 1903 there were 3,822 reported injuries in coal mines.

The production of coal in South Wales was at a high with 54 million tons in 1923. Twenty years later annual production had fallen to 25 million tons. In the fifteen years leading up to 1936 the number of working miners in South Wales fell from 270,000 to 130,000 and 241 mines were closed. This was the Great Depression when unemployment was rife in the South Wales Coalfield and where families struggled to live on their wages and unemployment pay. Almost 250,000 people found themselves out of work at the height of the Depression in 1933, more than a third of the workforce. In some places the figures were even worse – in Dowlais in the early 1930s, nearly three quarters were jobless. Many tried to flee this misery and left to find jobs in more affluent parts of England, with as many as 500,000 leaving South Wales between the two world wars.

I do have many cherished memories of the time I worked as a miner in the South Wales Coalfield, although unfortunately it brought my working life to an end.

Gerald Sullivan
Former coal miner

Introduction

I consider it an honour to be asked to write this introduction to David Owen's book on disasters and accidents in the South Wales Coalfield.

When I left school at sixteen years of age in 1979, going straight down the pit was not what I had in mind. I thought at the time there would be no future in the coal mining industry as British Coal were closing collieries all over South Wales and there was only just a handful of pits left producing coal. But it turned out for some unknown reason that I started work at Mardy Colliery, probably the most historical and famous pit in the world. It was the colliery where my father Ieuan 'Chick' Earland worked as an official of the mine who, incidentally, was the last man to knock all the power off at the colliery when the it had ceased production. He worked for thirty-five years in the pits. My grandfather Tom 'Chick' Earland worked at Ferndale No.5 Pit, Tylorstown No.9 Pit and Mardy Pit where he was a supervising collier on the training face in the Nine-Feet until he fractured his femur and could not work again.

It was a sad and emotional time for the folk of the Rhondda Valley and everyone involved in the mining industry when Mardy Colliery closed. Coal mining and its way of life in the Rhondda Valley had finally come to an end.

When one is working underground, there are only steel arches supporting the roof between the miner and the millions of tons of rock and earth of Glamorganshire above and, with the constant fear of falls or even explosions, keeping alert for danger and being safety conscious were always on my mind.

Some of the incidents at Mardy I recall were told to me by my father. In 1965 Howard 'Chippo' Jones and Harry Millard were working in the F13 when there was an explosion which was caused by shotfiring. Fortunately no one lost their life and in 1977 just before I started work at Mardy Colliery an accident occurred, seriously injuring three men and injuring three others. A runaway pair of tubs went out of control down a drift, striking some of the injured and trapping two others. I knew the miners involved; they were Dennis Piper, 'Merky' Jones, 'Snowy' Cavell, Jim Hayes, Glyn James and Gwyn 'Sheep' Rossiter. But the disaster that springs to most villagers' minds was the explosion at Mardy No.1 and No.2 Colliery just before Christmas on 23 December 1885 which killed eighty-one miners.

There is a camaraderie and good friendship that comes from everyone working at the pit; you were able to rely on everyone else for help, even in the most trying of conditions. Just descending the shaft and walking the four miles over rough terrain to the coalface, you need to have your wits about you, even today, after all the years of technological advancement.

Nearly every Monday morning, myself and my butty Brian 'Tab' Evans would be working in the tail road, the worse for wear from the night before, but still with enough energy to blast out a few ballads, although the other boys did not enjoy them.

After the miners' strike, I moved from Mardy Colliery to Tower Colliery, which is now the last deep coal mine in South Wales and the only workers' owned colliery in the world.

In 1962 an explosion occurred at Tower Colliery, killing nine miners and injuring nine other miners, another painful chapter in our lives.

Now, twenty-five years on from when I started, I can honestly say that I would not have given up the experience of being a miner for the world.

Chris Earland (Registration No.082)
Planned Maintenance Controller at Tower Colliery

Fifteen-year-old John 'Hank' Hanley,
Graham Clements and Ken Screech on
top of Ferndale No.5 Pit in 1954.

Fifteen-year-old John 'Hank' Hanley on
top of Ferndale No.5 Pit in 1954.

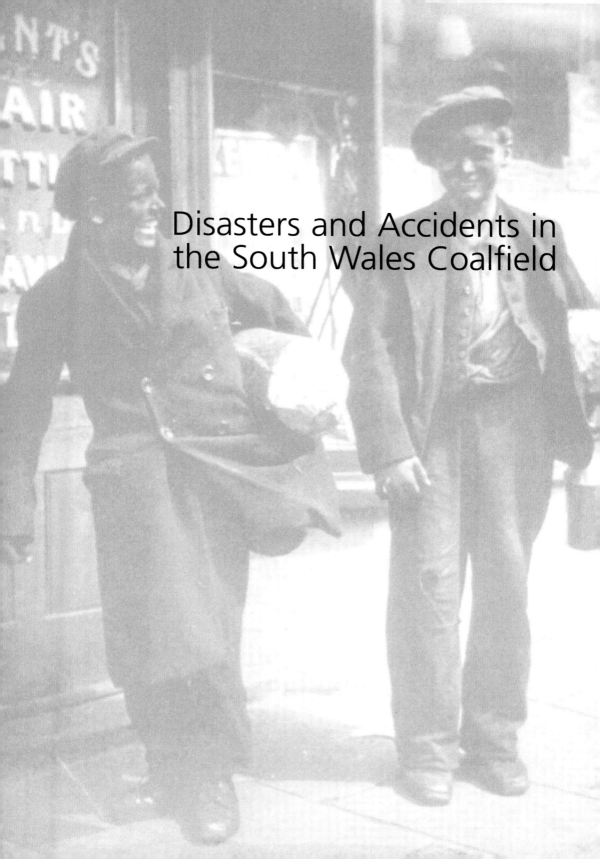

Disasters and Accidents in the South Wales Coalfield

Disasters and accidents were followed by other common ailments suffered by miners, namely ruptures, rheumatism and blood poisoning. On average, during the forty-six years before the First World War, one miner was killed every six hours, with a further twelve being seriously injured daily. In the year 1892, it was estimated that the ratio between fatal and non-fatal accidents was one hundred to one. Invariably, mine owners did not keep records, and thus such a ratio must be regarded as extremely conservative. An indication as to the true enormity of the problem can perhaps be shown best from the medical histories of valley general practitioners. Within a twelve-month period alone one Glamorganshire doctor treated over 500 cases of serious injury and, of these, 460 were directly attributable to mining accidents.

The causes of death underground were many and varied, but almost half of the fatalities recorded were as a result of roof falls. Explosions, although dramatic in the number of victims they claimed, accounted for fewer than 17 per cent of all deaths. Another major cause was from falls, which accounted for 12 per cent. Too often these deaths were the result of negligence in the form of unguarded shafts and crevices, and the parting of faulty winding ropes. Boiler and machinery explosions, falling debris and crushing by drams or moving machinery resulted in a further 27 per cent of all recorded deaths. Analysis of these grim statistics showed that 60 per cent of the victims were killed before reaching the age of thirty, and 80 per cent died by the time they were forty.

Living conditions throughout the mining communities were, by any standards, appalling. The hastily-erected terraced dwellings which housed a rapidly growing population soon became hopelessly overcrowded. The two- and three-roomed cottages were often home to several families, with ten or more people sharing a room. In addition to this, sanitation, where it existed, was at best elementary, with one lavatory serving the needs of an entire row of houses. Inevitably, such cramped living conditions, coupled with an inadequate diet and absence of proper medical care, resulted in poor standards of health throughout the whole community. Water supplies were usually obtained from a nearby well or stream and with the expanding population these soon became fouled by overflow from the communal cesspits. Such primitive facilities provided an ideal breeding ground for the proliferation of virulent bacteria, which, in turn, brought disease, despair and death to the inhabitants of the densely populated communities.

The hot summer of 1849 saw an outbreak of cholera that ravaged the towns of Merthyr, Dowlais and Aberdare. Within two months, 2,211 cases were reported, of which 884 resulted in death. Attempts to clean up the filth from the streets and open areas had little effect. Within five years, a second epidemic broke out which resulted in another heavy loss of life.

Similar conditions occurred in Cardiff, which by this time had also become a rapidly growing community which was built on the wealth created by the slaves of the golden nuggets from the hewing of coal.

Aberfan, Taff Vale, Glamorganshire

The last major disaster in the South Wales Coalfield and the one which, more than any other, broke the heart of a nation – Aberfan, Taff Vale, Glamorganshire – became the worst mining catastrophe in the history of industrial Britain, with its appalling toll of 144, including 114 school children, two children not yet of school age and twenty-eight adults, six of them teachers. This date must never be forgotten. What made the tragedy at Aberfan all the more poignant was that, more than any other in the South Wales coal industry, it was avoidable. 21 October is the date in the history of the South Wales Coalfield which, for sheer horror, surpasses all others. On that date the anonymity of a small Welsh mining community was lost forever. Front pages of newspapers the world over carried headlines of shock, disbelief and sympathy.

John Nixon began sinking Merthyr Vale Colliery with his partners on 23 August 1869 but before his arrival the tiny community of Aberfan consisted of only two cottages and an inn overlooking a green and pleasant land. Yet, following Nixon's sinking of the colliery, the landscape had been transformed by the growth of ugly slag heaps (tips) which destroyed the natural beauty of the valley.

Such was the horror that unfolded on that cold, damp, grey October morning that it is hardly surprising that, even today, some villagers still cannot talk about what happened. Yet it is impossible not to remember the children of Aberfan alongside all those other thousands who gave their lives for coal. They had been looking forward to their half-term holiday that morning, arriving at Pantglas Junior School for what was only due to have been a half-day. But high above them, among the tips that towered over the village, the tragedy was swiftly unfolding.

The No.7 Pantglas Tip had been shrouded in controversy since its origins five years earlier. There was already evidence that previous tips built there had been constructed on boggy ground. Years later it was revealed that the No.7 Tip itself had an underground mountain stream bubbling away directly underneath it. But, despite protest, work went ahead on the new tip in 1961. The following year, the National Coal Board (NCB) began using it to deposit 'tailings', minute particles of coal and ash which, when wet, took on a consistency similar to quicksand.

21 October had dawned cold, misty and overcast, 3ins of rain having fallen in the previous week. Engineers at work on the No.7 Tip had arrived there at 7.30 a.m. to find a 30ft crater in the centre. Supervisors were summoned to survey the situation but, at almost the moment they arrived at 9.00 a.m. a huge wave burst from the tip, carrying with it hundreds of tons of debris. The black torrent raced towards the still hidden village, engulfed hillside cottages and uprooted trees which stood in its path. The slithering mass formed a wall some 30ft high, carrying beneath it the debris of the demolished houses that had crumpled in its relentless advance. It sped towards Pantglas Junior School, crushing the walls and roof of the school without faltering. All emergency services had been alerted. On hearing the news Merthyr Vale miners rushed to the stricken village, where residents had begun tearing at the mountain of rubble with their bare hands. It was the colliers, most still black from their work underground, who gave their expertise and provided invaluable assistance by directing the essential digging operations. Side by side miners, frantic parents and inquisitive onlookers dug in a desperate attempt to uncover those buried beneath the falls of rubble.

The news of the disaster reached far and wide, and people began to flock to the scene. Most came to offer help, others simply to stare. The first message of Royal sympathy came from the Prince of Wales. A disaster fund was set up by the Mayor of Merthyr Tydfil and thousands of messages of condolence were received.

Thankfully, the tribunal which investigated the disaster agreed where the blame should be laid. The tribunal chairman said the NCB's liability was 'uncontestable'.

This is a sad reminder of the true price of coal, and one that must never, never happen again. The memorial plaque at the entrance to the Aberfan Memorial Garden reads:

PANTGLAS JUNIOR SCHOOL MEMORIAL GARDEN DEDICATED TO 116 CHILDREN AND 28 ADULTS WHO LOST THEIR LIVES 21ST OCTOBER 1966 TO THOSE WE LOVE AND MISS VERY MUCH I'R RHAI A GARWN AC Y GALARWYN O'U COLLI.

Tips and abandoned workings now lie hidden beneath the gentle slopes of reclamation; the industrial landscape of Wales has reverted to being green and lush and nature has returned as a result. We retain our sense of pride and traditional heritage but combine it with a new optimism.

Abergwawr Colliery, Aberaman, Cynon Valley, Glamorganshire

Abergwawr Colliery, Aberaman, was locally known as Plough Pit and was sunk in 1854 by Thomas Powell. The colliery was also owned by the Powell Duffryn Steam Coal Co. In 1872 the accident reports show that a ten-year-old boy was killed underground by a fall of roof and on 7 January 1873 the accident reports show that twenty-five-year-old labourer Samuel Rees was killed underground by a journey of drams. Abergwawr Colliery was closed in 1886.

Abernant No.9 Colliery, Abernant, Cynon Valley, Glamorganshire

Abernant No.9 Colliery was sunk in 1871 by the Abernant Iron Co. On 16 May 1890 the accident reports show that twenty-seven-year-old ripper W. Thomas and twenty-three-year-old haulier W. Rees were killed by an explosion of firedamp. Abernant Colliery was closed in 1901.

Albion Colliery, Cilfynydd, Taff Vale, Glamorganshire

The Albion Colliery in the Taff Valley was situated in close proximity to Abercynon Colliery and was sunk from 1884 to 1887 when the two shafts reached a depth of 1,900ft. It was opened by the Albion Steam Coal Co. which went into liquidation in 1928. The colliery was bought by the Powell Duffryn Steam Coal Co. (PDs Poverty and Dole).

On Saturday 23 June 1894 at approximately 3.50 p.m. an explosion killed 290 men and boys in the No.1 district called Grover's Level. The No.1 district had forty-one working places. The explosion occurred in the Four-Feet coal seam, which was at a depth of 545 yards from the surface, the thickness of the seam varied from between 5ft 10ins and 6ft 10ins. Grover's level had reached 1,136 yards from the shafts on the western side of the pit. Apart from the deaths of six men in two separate accidents when the pit was sunk, Albion Colliery was to remain untouched by the spectre of death for the first few years of its life. At 3.50 p.m., nearly two hours after the afternoon shift had descended to repair the roadways and remove dust, two loud reports were heard above ground in quick succession. These were followed immediately by a charge of dust and smoke from the downcast shaft and then from the upcast shaft. Men on the surface near the shafts were blown backwards by the blasts and temporarily blinded by the dust. No flame was reported, but it was quite probable that some flame reached the top of the downcast shaft for those there declared they had felt the heat of the blast and two of them complained that their eyelashes had been singed. The muffled roar of an explosion, followed by a tremor, shook the whole valley, and brought inhabitants of the village hurrying to their doors. Like so many of the narrow mining valleys of South Wales, the small terraced cottages perched precariously on the steep hillsides overlooking the pit. From such a vantage point, those who looked onto the valley below saw dense swirling clouds of smoke shrouding the shafts. The whole community held its breath and feared the worst. The news soon began to reach those outside the community, and crowds began to arrive in their hundreds, from the Cynon Valley, Pontypridd and Rhondda Valley and the Merthyr Valleys. Messages of sympathy flowed into the stunned community; one was sent on behalf of Queen Victoria.

By 6 July the total number of fatalities was put at 279, although twenty-five men were still unaccounted for. The situation was not helped by the fact that several of the victims had been buried without being identified. As work on clearing the mine progressed, two more victims were located and brought to the surface. These, together with the death of one of the remaining survivors, brought the official figure of those who perished in the disaster to 290. The pit ponies that had been in the deep were found alive. The Coroner's findings were recorded thus: the cause of the explosion was unknown, but it was believed to have been caused by the ignition of coal dust following an explosion of firedamp. The colliery was reopened within two weeks following the explosion on 23 June 1894 and some changes in safety took place. The old spray system had not proved successful and was replaced by hosepipes and the coal drams had been altered to prevent coal falling on the roadways and being crushed into fine dust. The safety Clanny lamp that was used had a single gauze and an automatic lock that could be opened only by a powerful electro-magnet. The lamps were lit by an electric spark from an apparatus consisting of a square iron box with a locked door. On top of the box was a dish on which was placed the lamp to be relit. In the box was a double accumulator connected to an induction coil, the accumulator being charged with four volts. The current could be increased to the coil by up to 10,000 volts. If a lamp was not placed correctly on the dish on top of the box, the spark produced to light it would fail to pass through an insulated pin and ignite the wick, but would instead make contact between the lamp housing and the coil. If gas was present then there could be disastrous results.

The explosion at Albion Colliery on Saturday 10 November 1906 at approximately 3.10 a.m. claimed the following six miners' lives:

Names of casualties	Age	Occupation
1. James Henry Hill	53	overman
2. Richard Hughes	33	timberman
3. John Jones	36	ripper
4. Abraham Lloyd	21	assistant timberman
5. Thomas Prosser	41	master haulier
6. Francis Strong	40	assistant timberman

The overman James Henry Hill was sent underground to investigate and found a large fall in the main roadway, but was able to bypass it by going through another heading. He came to the lamp

Albion Colliery in 1900.

station and found five very badly burned workmen. Three were dead and the other two died in their homes within forty-eight hours. Henry Hill continued to search, but went missing and a rescue party found his body later. He had died from the effects of afterdamp. On 26 November the following verdict was recorded by the jury:

> In view of the theory advanced by Mr Lewis, the agent of the colliery, supported by HM Inspectors, that the explosion was probably caused by the emission of sparks from the electric battery, we are agreed upon that theory and that no fault or negligence can be attached to any persons concerned.

It appears that the relighter had been put in what the manager considered was a safe place in the intake nine months prior to the accident. The box was kept locked so as not to be available for use except by the person authorised by the manager to relight lamps. It had, however, been removed from its brick built casing at 2.00 p.m. on the day of the explosion for fear of a fall of roof which might occur when timbers were removed as part of the repair programme. According to the manager, even if the relighter had not been removed from its original position the man in charge would have taken the extinguished lamps to it and the same result would have ensued. Everyone agreed with this, but between the accident and the resumed inquest the manager reported that all relighters in the colliery had been removed and resited near the downcast shaft. Albion Colliery was closed in September 1966 by the NCB.

Black Vein Colliery, Risca, near Crosskeys, Ebbw Fawr Valley, Monmouthshire

Black Vein Colliery was opened in 1841. At 8.00 a.m. on Wednesday 14 January 1846, there was an explosion at the colliery at the foot of Machen Mountain which killed thirty-five men and boys.

The colliery was once known as Waun Fawr Pit. It was sunk and owned by a local consortium headed by Mr John Russell, he who, in partnership with Mr Brown, was a one-time proprietor of the Blaina Ironworks. Mr Russell was said to be overwhelmed with grief at the magnitude of the disaster.

The explosion at Black Vein Colliery on 14 January 1846 claimed the following thirty-five men and boys' lives:

Names of casualties	Marital status	Names of casualties	Marital status
1. John Attwell	single	19. James Gambel	married
2. George Banfield	married	20. James Gullock	married
3. Thomas Banfield	single	21. William Harrison	single
4. George Banfield jnr	single	22. Charles Hearns	single
5. John Bath	single	23. Jesse Hodges	married
6. Isaac Bryant	married	24. Elias Jones	single
7. William Bryant	single	25. James Lane	married
8. Samuel Bryant	single	26. Isaac Lovel	married
9. Charles Collier	single	27. James Pike	married
10. Emanuel Crook	single	28. John Pool	married
11. James Crook	single	29. John Powell	married
12. John Crook	married	30. Samuel Silcox	single
13. George Curtis	married	31. George Summers	married
14. John Danks	married	32. William Thomas	single
15. Daniel Danks snr	married	33. John Walls	married
16. John Danks jnr	single	34. George Williams	single
17. John Evans	married	35. Thomas Woodward	married
18. Isaac Fuidge	single		

On Saturday 12 March 1853, there was another explosion at Black Vein Colliery which claimed the lives of ten men and boys, some of whom were only twelve years old. This explosion occurred at the entrance to No.13 heading about half a mile from pit bottom. Mr Green the agent immediately led a rescue party into the district. He was forced to retreat from his effort, exceedingly weakened by the afterdamp. The gas was ignited by the candle of Thomas Davies. An air door had been left open.

The explosion claimed the lives of the following ten men and boys:

Names of casualties	Age	Occupation			
1. Aaron Bryan	22	collier	8. George Phillips	19	haulier
2. Joseph Bryant	24	collier	9. George Purnell	11	doorboy
3. Samuel Dack	12	collier's boy	10. John Williams	44	collier
4. Rees Davies	24	collier			
5. Thomas Davies	40	collier	*Names of injured*		
6. Solomon Jenkins	20	collier	1. William Beachan, young boy		
7. Moses Moore	12	doorboy	2. John Chivers		
			3. James Christopher, young boy		

4. David Morgan, young boy
5. John Porch
6. William Purnell, young boy
7. Henry Purnell
The verdict was accidental death.

8. Richard Richards
9. Alfred Sims
10. Samuel Williams

On Saturday 1 December 1860, there was another explosion at Black Vein Colliery which claimed the lives of 142 men and boys, including eleven-year-old Frederick Norris, eleven-year-old Henry Thomas and eleven-year-old George West, who could only be identified because he was known to be the only one to wear Wellington boots. A journalistic statement at the time perhaps reflects the emphasis on the social climate of the day, by reporting the harsh financial loss incurred on the colliery mine owner with the deaths of twenty-eight pit ponies, with a value of almost £1,000.

The explosion at Black Vein Colliery on 11 December 1860 claimed the lives of the following 142 men and boys:

Names of casualties	Age	Cause of death	Names of casualties	Age	Cause of death
1. David Bailey	27	blackdamp	33. William Davies	22	blackdamp
2. John Banfield	40	blackdamp	34. Henry Edwards	39	blackdamp
3. Joseph Banfield		blackdamp	35. Jonathan Edwards	29	blackdamp
4. William Banfield		blackdamp	36. David Edwards		blackdamp
5. Isaac Bateman		blackdamp	37. Edward English	41	blackdamp
6. Levi Bateman		blackdamp	38. Thomas Evans	20	blackdamp
7. William Bath	31	blackdamp	39. Charles Evans		blackdamp
8. Thomas Bath	15	blackdamp	40. Joseph Evans		blackdamp
9. Evan Beddoe	43	fractured skull	41. Isaac Evans		blackdamp
10. Stephen Beddoe	17	blackdamp	42. George Fisher	18	blackdamp
11. William Bevan		blackdamp	43. James Fisher		blackdamp
12. Elijah Binding	36	blackdamp	44. John Fisher		blackdamp
13. Enock Binding	34	blackdamp	45. George Golding	23	blackdamp
14. Joshua Binding	36	blackdamp	46. Henry Golding		blackdamp
15. Joseph Bowen		blackdamp	47. George Gough	18	blackdamp
16. Mark Brace		blackdamp	48. John Griffiths	23	blackdamp
17. James Brimble	35	blackdamp	49. James Grindle		blackdamp
18. Thomas Brimble	12	blackdamp	50. Joseph Grindle		blackdamp
19. William Brimble	13	burnt	51. Frederick Gullick		blackdamp
20. Benjamin Britain	22	blackdamp	52. Charles Hale	34	blackdamp
21. Moses Bryant	49	blackdamp	53. William. Hale		blackdamp
22. Thomas Bullock		blackdamp	54. James Hammond	25	burnt
23. Samuel Chivers		blackdamp	55. John Harris	41	blackdamp
24. Henry Court	13	blackdamp	56. John Harris	32	burnt
25. James Cousener	28	blackdamp	57. William Harris	43	blackdamp
26. Charles Cox		blackdamp	58. Edwin Holder	21	blackdamp
27. John Crew	34	burnt	59. William Hughes	40	blackdamp
28. Emanuel Crew	34	blackdamp	60. Morgan Hughes	39	blackdamp
29. Alfred Davies	24	blackdamp	61. Joseph Jacques		blackdamp
30. Hopkin Davies		blackdamp	62. Henry James	45	blackdamp
31. William Davies	35	burnt	63. David Jenkins	28	blackdamp
32. William Davies		blackdamp	64. Phillip Jenkins	22	blackdamp

Names of casualties	Age	Cause of death	Names of casualties	Age	Cause of death
65. William Jenkins	24	blackdamp	105. George Robbins	38	blackdamp
66. Thomas Jenkins	24	blackdamp	106. Gethin Roberts		blackdamp
67. Richard Jenkins		blackdamp	107. Thomas Rosser		blackdamp
68. William John	23	blackdamp	108. Isaac Sage	32	blackdamp
69. William Jones	42	blackdamp	109. George Sage		blackdamp
70. John Jones	16	blackdamp	110. John Sage		blackdamp
71. John Jones	29	blackdamp	111. Isaac Saunders	42	blackdamp
72. Thomas Jones		blackdamp	112. Llewellyn Saunders		blackdamp
73. Thomas Jones	21	blackdamp	113. George Skidmore	35	blackdamp
74. William Jones		blackdamp	114. Llewellyn Thomas	15	burnt
75. John Jones		blackdamp	115. Henry Thomas	11	blackdamp
76. William Kealing	18	blackdamp	116. James Turner		blackdamp
77. Nathaniel King		blackdamp	117. John Watts	15	blackdamp
78. Charles Ledbury	24	blackdamp	117. John Watts	15	blackdamp
79. James Lewis	41	blackdamp	118. Nathaniel Watkins		blackdamp
80. George Lewis	19	blackdamp	119. Isaac Watson		blackdamp
81. William Lewis	28	burnt	120. Abraham Watson	32	blackdamp
82. John Lippiett		blackdamp	121. Isaac Watson	12	blackdamp
83. John Morgan	35	blackdamp	122. George Watson	10	blackdamp
84. John Murray	23	blackdamp	123. George Webb	40	blackdamp
85. Thomas Nelmes	22	burnt	124. John West	24	blackdamp
86. George Newport	27	burnt	125. Joseph West	13	blackdamp
87. James Nicholas	17	blackdamp	126. George West	11	blackdamp
88. Frederick Norris	11	blackdamp	127. Frederick White		blackdamp
89. Aaron Parry	15	blackdamp	128. Charles White	17	blackdamp
90. George Pearce	13	blackdamp	129. Daniel Wilkins	41	burnt
91. William Perry	13	blackdamp	130. John Williams	26	burnt
92. James Phillips	20	blackdamp	131. William Williams	17	blackdamp
93. John Phillips		blackdamp	132. John Williams	31	blackdamp
94. John Phillips	35	blackdamp	133. John Williams	17	blackdamp
95. John Phillips	26	blackdamp	134. William Williams	55	blackdamp
96. George Pike	52	blackdamp	135. William Williams		blackdamp
97. James Plumber		blackdamp	136. Edmund Williams		blackdamp
98. James Pritchard	15	blackdamp	137. Thomas Williams		blackdamp
99. Jenkin Pritchard	27	blackdamp	138. William Wilson	18	burnt
100. Thomas Prosser	22	blackdamp	139. John Wilton	29	blackdamp
101. Henry Purnell		blackdamp	140. William Wilton	12	blackdamp
102. Daniel Rees	17	blackdamp	141. Thomas Wizard		blackdamp
103. Abraham Rees	31	blackdamp	142. John Woolley	17	burnt
104. Rees Morgan Rees	27	blackdamp			

It was a bitterly cold morning when Charles Harrison began his descent down the shaft at Black Vein Colliery. Work had, as usual, started early that Saturday, 1 December 1860, the miners beginning their shift an hour earlier to allow a midday finish. Having made the rounds that morning he had ensured that the air pumped through the maze of drifts was of sufficient strength to disperse any lethal accumulation of gas. His routine examination completed, Charles Harrison's thoughts now turned to his breakfast. When he reached the surface he sat down to eat with his son. Breakfast over, the men parted, George returning down the mine while his father headed for Rock Vein Pit to continue his safety checks. However, before he had reached the other mine, a banksman stopped him and informed him that an explosion had just occurred back at Black Vein Colliery. Since he had carried out thorough safety checks less than an hour previously, he found this beyond his comprehension. Yet such was the insistence of the banksman, Charles Harrison hastily returned. The time was a few minutes after 9:30 a.m. When he reached the pit his initial assessment was one of chaos. He was informed that a terrific booming noise came bellowing up the shaft which had caused instant alarm and intense anxiety. The worst was feared. Along with several rescuers, Charles Harrison made the perilous descent into the darkened pit shaft. His concern lay not only for his own son, but also for the other 142 men and boys at risk. His son George Harrison survived the explosion.

Lord Tredegar made available a plot of land in which the victims could be interred; however, many of those who had died were returned to their home towns. Black Vein Colliery was closed in the 1920s.

Cambrian Colliery, Clydach Vale, Rhondda Valley, Glamorganshire.

Cambria Colliery Explosion 1905

The night was lonely and black when a sudden explosion below ground brought sorrow to the coal-mining valleys of Wales.

In 1872 Samuel Thomas and J. Osborne Riches of the Cwmclydach Colliery Co. and Thomas Joseph of Aberdare sank the No.1 shaft and in 1874 struck the Six-Feet coal seam. The No.2 shaft was opened in 1875 and in 1899 the two pits produced over 1,000 tons of coal per day. The No.3 shaft was sunk in 1889 and completed in 1891. In 1910 the manpower in No.1 Pit was 701, in No.2 Pit 1,498 and in No.3 Pit 1,855. On 7 August 1874 the accident reports show that collier J. Powell was killed underground by a fall of stone and on 7 March 1876 the accident reports show that collier John Thomas died the same way. On 10 March 1905 an explosion killed thirty-three men and boys and on 17 May 1965 another explosion killed thirty-one miners.

The explosion at Cambrian Colliery on 10 March 1905 claimed the lives of the following thirty-three men and boys:

Names of injured		Occupation	Residence	
Name	*Age*	*Occupation*	*Residence, marital status*	*Nature of injuries, cause of death*
1. Joseph Chalker	33	ostler	14 Park Terrace, Clydach Vale, married with two children	Body charred and mummified caused by extreme heat.
2. Evan Davies	42	night fireman	50 Charles Street, Tonypandy, married with three children	Body not recovered. Poisoning by carbon monoxide.
3. Jenkin Davies	49	night repairer	17 Adam Street, Clydach Vale, married with three children	Hair singed, face burnt, cherry red in appearance caused by poisoning by carbon monoxide.
4. Thomas Davies	21	day collier	17 Wern Terrace, Clydach Vale, single	Hair singed, burnt face, fractures of pelvis, thighs and legs, nails bluish caused by violence.

Name	Age	Occupation	Residence, marital status	Nature of injuries, cause of death
5. Noah Edmunds	48	night repairer	22 Marian Street, Clydach Vale, single	Hair singed, face swollen. Nails pink caused by poisoning by carbon monoxide.
6. David Enoch	35	night repairer	3 High Street, Clydach Vale, single	Body very swollen and decomposed. Head partly scalped, fatty heart, anaemic, liver enlarged and black, no fracture caused by shock.
7. Evan Evans	36	night labourer	57 Gelli Road, Ton Pentre, married with one child	Hair singed, face burnt, cherry red in appearance caused by poisoning by carbon monoxide.
8. William Evans	45	night repairer	104 Marian Street, Clydach Vale, single	Face congested, veins of upper parts of face and chest full of dark red blood caused by absence of oxygen caused by acute suffocation.
9. John Griffiths	40	shoeing smith	94 High Street, Clydach Vale, married no children	Body charred and mummified caused by extreme heat.
10. William Griffiths	60	night locker	53 Marian Street, Clydach Vale, married, no children	Face congested, dark red lips. Decomposition set in. Blood in aorta congested and dark red caused by absence of oxygen caused by acute suffocation.
11. William Gronow	51	night haulier	40 Howard Terrace, Clydach Vale, married with three children	Hair burnt off face, compound fracture of femur. Cherry red in appearance caused by carbon monoxide poisoning and violence.
12. Morgan Harding	47	night master haulier	43 Bush Houses, Clydach Vale, married with three children	Hair singed, face, hands and chest burnt, burns on leg, developed septic pneumonia. Rescued alive, died nine days later from burns.
13. Henry Harvey	45	night haulier	9 Tram Road Side, Dinas, married with four children	Hair singed, face and hands burnt, fracture of both legs, right leg dislocated at hip joint caused by violence.
14. Thomas Hawkins	48	ostler	28 Bush Houses, Clydach Vale, married with one child	Body charred and mummified caused by extreme heat.
15. William Harris	33	night fireman	87 High Street, Clydach Vale, married with one child	Hair singed, hands burnt Decomposition to no great extent. Muscular tissue cherry red caused by poisoning by carbon monoxide.
16. Thomas John	36	night hitcher	62 Marian Street, Clydach Vale, married with seven children	Fractures everywhere. No burns caused by violence.
17. Edward Jones	47	night repairer	133 Cemetery Road, Porth, married with four children	Badly burned and singed, nails and lips pink. Disembowelled

Name	Age	Occupation	Residence, marital status	Nature of injuries, cause of death
				caused by carbon monoxide poisoning and violence.
18. John Jones	38	night repairer	57 Court Street, Tonypandy, married with four children	Hair singed, face swollen. Nails pink caused by poisoning of carbon monoxide.
19. Joseph Jones	50	night brattice -man	24 Marian Street, Clydach Vale, married with three children	Right arm and scapula first found. Both arms fractured, part of occipital and parietal bones found. Other parts of his body were in parcels caused by extreme violence.
20. Adam Lewis	45	night labourer	90 Jones Street, Clydach Vale, single	Hair singed, face and hands burned, left arm broken. Face cherry red appearance caused by carbon monoxide poisoning.
21. David Lewis	55	night repairer	37 Clydach Road, Clydach Vale, married with no children	Hair singed, wound round liver, skull at base fractured. Cherry red appearance, blood fluid cause by violence and carbon monoxide poisoning.
22. Rees Lewis	53	night brattice -man	98 Wern Street, Clydach Vale, married with three children	Upper part of chest and head burnt. Hair singed, fractures of right arm, leg and thigh. Pectoral muscle cherry red. Pericardium cherry red, also heart caused by poisoning by carbon monoxide.
23. William Lewis	39	night brattice -man	46 Court Street, Tonypandy, married with three children	Hair burnt, brain protruding beneath skull, lower and upper jaws fractured, ribs badly smashed. Heart and liver found in abdominal cavity. Pelvis fractured. Right and left legs fractured. Shoulders and right arm torn from body caused by extreme violence.
24. David Morgan	35	night rider	43 Primrose Street, Tonypandy, married with four children	Body not recovered.
25. Thomas Morgan	26	shoeing smith	51 Clydach Road, Clydach Vale, single	Body charred and mummified caused by extreme heat.
26. John Owen	50	night repairer	21 Evans Terrace, Trealaw, married with six children	Hair singed and poisoned by carbon monoxide.
27. John Ridge	50	night ripper	133 Primrose Street, Tonypandy, married with one child	Badly burnt, fracture of thigh, occipital bone depressed caused by violence.
28. Thomas Richards	42	night fireman	11 Park Terrace, Clydach Vale, married with seven children	Hair singed, face, hands, chest and thighs burnt, whole muscular tissue cherry red in colour caused

Name	Age	Occupation	Residence, marital status	Nature of injuries, cause of death
				by poisoning by carbon monoxide.
29. Frank Shallish	45	ostler	104 Clydach Road, Clydach Vale, married with five children	Body charred and mummified caused by extreme heat.
30. Edwin Thomas	33	night hitcher	76 Marian Street, Clydach Vale, married with eight children	Face burnt, hair singed. Fracture of pelvis caused by violence.
31. William H. Tudball	42	night fireman	63 Court Street, Tonypandy, married with two children	Right ankle and left leg fractured. Left thigh and upper part of chest burnt. Fingers of both hands burnt and fractured. Heart bright cherry red in appearance. Blood in cavities of heart, bright red and fluid. Pleura cherry red caused by poisoning by carbon monoxide.
32. Owen Williams	24	night ripper	90 Marian Street, Clydach Vale, single	Hair singed, face burnt. Nails pink caused by poisoning of carbon monoxide.
33. Robert Williams	23	night labourer	40 Railway Terrace, Clydach Vale, single	Hair singed, face burnt. Cherry red in appearance caused by poisoning by carbon monoxide.

1. George Brace — day pulleyman — 61 Wern Terrace, Clydach Vale
2. John Davies — night repairer — 55 Court Street, Tonypandy
3. Thomas Evans — night haulier — 55 Court Street, Tonypandy
4. David Griffiths — night repairer — 91 Wern Street, Clydach Vale
5. John Griffiths — night haulier — 58 Marian Street, Clydach Vale
6. James Hall — day collier — 33 High Street, Clydach Vale
7. John Jones — day roadman — 15 Railway Terrace, Clydach Vale
8. Robert Jones — night assistant repairer — 50 Marian Street, Clydach Vale
9. John Lloyd — night ripperman — 26 Adam Street, Clydach Vale
10. Richard Pugh — night repairer — 54 Charles Street, Tonypandy
11. Lewis Thomas — night repairer — 24 Wern Street, Clydach Vale
12. Morgan Thomas — night master haulier — 1 Bush Houses, Clydach Vale
13. Thomas Thomas — day pulleyman — 27 Howard Terrace, Clydach Vale
14. David Wild — day assistant collier — 52 Moreton Street, Clydach Vale

Cambrian Colliery Explosion 1965

The explosion at Cambrian Colliery on Monday 17 May 1965 claimed the following thirty-one miners' lives:

Names of casualties	Age	Occupation (deputy is a management official)
1. Ronald Arnold	48	deputy (*employed to carry out safety inspections*)
2. Mr Ernest John Breeze	38	manager (*especially to detect the presence of gas*)
3. Ernest William Burnett	46	chargeman (*in charge of conveyor belts*)
4. Peter Calvert	40	repairer (*a miner employed to repair and replace damaged roof supports*)
5. James Channing	46	poster
6. Albert William Colcombe	44	team captain
7. Raymond John Daniels	34	stableman
8. Gerrard Wayne Davies	24	assistant unit electrical engineer
9. Kenneth Davies	26	plough operator
10. David Evans	28	poster
11. Ronald Flower	45	repairer
12. Ronald Gregson	28	electrician
13. David Alfred Griffiths	43	repairer
14. Thomas Hann	42	transfer point attendant (*conveyor operator*)
15. Richard William Hucker	32	repairer
16. Ivor Jacobs	45	poster
17. Henry Lee	56	roadman (*maintaining the rail network*)
18. Leonard May	33	poster (*the poster erects hydraulic props which are manually pumped against roof bars of steel, with a key. It was also a safer, easier method of extraction*)
19. Ivor Morgan	32	poster
20. Arthur James Newman	46	poster
21. Vivian Nicholas	51	poster
22. Harold David Pope	50	overman (*official oversees the work of miners*)
23. Donald Price	42	stableman (*makes room for conveyors and*
24. Evan Luther Rees	48	poster *coalcutters on the end of a coal face*)
25. Richard John Roberts	55	repairer
26. Gwilym Thomas	28	assistant stableman
27. William Isaac Thomas	33	poster
28. Edmund William Williams	51	repairer
29. Leslie James Williams	54	undermanager
30. Sidney Williams	47	poster
31. Trevor John Williams	27	poster

Seriously injured

Thomas Rees	62	a rider (*responsible for safe movement of drams*)

A seven-man jury solemnly listened as Coroner Alwyn T. John said, 'The grief and sorrow which has descended on so many homes in this valley as a result of the calamity shows what price is paid for the winning of coal measured in terms of human life'. The mile-long cortege made the silent two-mile walk to the cemetery. At the graveside, an estimated 5,000 people gathered to pay their respects. The following day saw a re-enactment of these events when more of the victims were laid to rest.

Cambrian Colliery was closed on Saturday 24 September 1966 by the NCB.

Coed Cae Colliery, Trehafod, Rhondda Valley, Glamorganshire

The Owners Edward Mills opened the Coed Cae Colliery in 1850. On 18 May 1872 the accident reports show that fifteen-year-old collier R. Thomas was killed underground by a fall of coal; on 11 February 1882 two explosions caused by naked lights killed six men and boys; the tremor was felt in Porth, the next village. On 24 August 1888 the accident reports show that thirteen-year-old collier boy Edward Richard was killed underground by a fall of clod (a thin layer of mudstone); on 20 October 1889 the accident reports show that twenty-seven-year-old sinker Ben Morris was killed by a fall of fireclay from the side of a sinking shaft. It fell upon him approximately 7ft from the bottom of the shaft and on 18 May 1893 the accident reports show that twenty-two-year-old collier Chris Mathews was injured underground by a fall of roof.

The two explosions (the first at approximately 7.00 a.m. and the second at 7.30 a.m.) at Coed Cae Colliery on Saturday 11 February 1882 claimed the following six miners' lives:

Names of casualties
1. Benjamin James
2. James Howell Lewis
3. George Marlow

Names of casualties
4. Joseph Rowlands
5. Jacob Thomas
6. Thomas Williams

Coed Cae Colliery Trehafod in 1900. The Owners Edward Mills opened the Coed Cae Colliery in 1850. In 1913 the manpower in the Coedcae was 556. On 18 May 1872 the accident reports show that fifteen-year-old collier R. Thomas was killed by a fall of coal. The Coed Cae Colliery ceased producing coal in 1929.

The inquest decided that the mine was 'Very carefully managed'. Coed Cae Colliery ceased producing coal in 1929.

Cwmbach Colliery, Cwmbach, Cynon Valley, Glamorganshire

Cwmbach Colliery was sunk in 1844. On 2 August 1845 an explosion claimed twenty-eight men and boys' lives; on 8 October 1852 twenty-six-year-old David Llewellyn and twenty-seven-year-old William Griffith (both colliers) were killed by an explosion of firedamp; on 12 September 1853 eleven-year-old doorboy John Evans was killed by an explosion of firedamp; on 15 February 1872 the accident reports show that twelve-year-old doorboy D. Evans was killed by a fall of roof; on 20 March 1872 the accident reports show that forty-five-year-old collier John Protheroe was crushed to death by a journey of drams and on 10 December 1872 the accident reports show that forty-four-year-old collier H. Griffiths was killed by a journey of drams while walking up an engine plane (main roadway). Cwmbach Colliery was closed in 1892.

Cymmer Colliery, Porth, Rhondda Valley, Glamorganshire

George Insole started to develop the Cymmer mines in 1844 when he opened the South Cymmer Level in the Rhondda No.2 coal seam. In 1847 he sank the No.1 or Old Cymmer Pit, which struck the Rhondda No.3 coal seam at 1,104ft; the section of coal was 38ins. In 1851 the Upper Cymmer Colliery was working at a depth of 372ft. In 1860 the Upper Cymmer Colliery was leased to T.C. Hinde but was back in the hands of the Cymmer Colliery Co. in 1889. The New Cymmer Colliery was sunk in 1886 with the final sinkings starting in 1875 with two shafts being sunk to 384 yards and later deepened to 435 yards. The coal seams worked were the Rhondda No.2 at a section of 36ins, the Two-Feet-Nine at 19ins, the Six-Feet at 109ins, the Five-Feet at 63ins, the Rhondda No.3 at 38ins, the Four-Feet at 53ins and the Nine-Feet at 69ins. At approximately 8.30 a.m. on 13 July 1856 an explosion in the west side of the pit shook the village and the surrounding area; some thought it was an earthquake. Even the birds hushed their singing and the valley became still and silent. The explosion killed 114 men and boys and eleven pit ponies; no person or living thing was spared in the west side of the pit.

The explosion at Cymmer Colliery on Sunday 13 July 1856 claimed the lives of the following 114 men and boys:

Names of casualties
1. Thomas Andrews
2. Dafydd Dafydd (ten years old)
3. Morgan Dafydd
4. Philip Dafydd
5. Thomas Dafydd snr
6. Thomas Dafydd jnr (twelve years old)
7. William Dafydd (David)

Names of casualties
8. Dafydd Daniel
9. Dafydd Davies
10. Daniel Davies
11. Hezekiah Davies
12. Hezekiah's son
13. Hezekiah's son
14. Thomas Davies jnr

15. William Davies
16. William Davies
17. Dafydd T. Dennis
18. Edward Dennis
19. Samuel Edmunds snr
20. Samuel Edmunds jnr
21. Thomas Edwards
22. Benjamin Evans
23. John Evans
24. John Evans
25. Mathew Evans
26. Morgan Evans
27. Philip Evans
28. William Evans
29. Benjamin Gibbon
30. George Griffiths
31. Henry Griffiths
32. John Griffiths
33. Peter Griffiths
34. Dafydd Harries
35. Thomas Hayman
36. Thomas Hopkins
37. Thomas Hopkins
38. D. Howell
39. E. Howell
40. Edward Howell
41. Evan Hugh
42. Richard Hugh
43. Edwin Hughes
44. Evan Hughes
45. Evan Hulan
46. John Isaac
47. Henry Jarvis
48. Dafydd Jenkins
49. John Jenkins
50. John Jenkins
51. Rees Jenkins
52. William Jenkins
53. William Jenkins
54. William Jenkins
55. Dafydd John
56. Joseph John
57. Thomas John (ten years old)
58. Henry Jones
59. William Jones
60. Daniel Lewis snr
61. Daniel Lewis jnr

62. Edward Lewis
63. Evan Lewis
64. Thomas Lewis
65. William Lewis
66. Thomas Llewellyn
67. William Llewellyn
68. William Llewellyn
69. William Martin
70. Thomas Mathews
71. Evan Miles
72. Richard Miles
73. Walter Miles
74. Walter Miles
75. Dafydd Morgan
76. DafyddMorgan
77. Enoch Morgan
78. Isaac Morgan
79. John Morgan
80. Morgan Morgan
81. Morgan Morgan
82. Thomas Morgan
83. William Morgan
84. Evan Phillips
85. Isaac Phillips
86. Dafydd Powell
87. Aaron Rees
88. Benjamin Rees
89. John Rees
90. Richard Rees
91. Thomas Rees
92. William Rees
93. Dafydd Richards
94. Zachariah Richards
95. John Roberts
96. Dafydd Samuel
97. Jacomi Samuel
98. John Salathiel
99. George Solloway
100. Henry Solloway
101. Dafydd Thomas
102. Daniel Thomas
103. Evan Thomas
104. Gomer Thomas
105. James Thomas
106. John Thomas
107. Llewellyn Thomas
108. Mathew Thomas

The inquest was held at the Tynewydd Hotel, Porth. The jury returned a verdict of manslaughter against the manager Jabez Thomas, the overman Rowland Rowlands, the fireman David Jones and the fireman William Thomas. The jury acquitted them. Cymmer Colliery was closed in 1940.

Dare Colliery, Cwmparc, Rhondda Valley, Glamorganshire

Sinking began in 1864 by David Davies and Co. (David Davies and Thomas Webb, Llandinam; Morgan Joseph, Ystradfechan; John Osborne Riches, Aberdare; Abraham Howell, Welshpool; and Ezra Roberts, Tenby). On 27 November 1873 the accident reports show that thirty-two-year-old rider David Bowen was killed by drams on the engine plane; on 2 March 1874 the accident reports show that twenty-two-year-old collier J. Harris was killed by a fall of coal. The Dare Colliery was closed with the Park Colliery in February 1966 by the NCB.

Darran Colliery, Deri, Darran Valley, Glamorganshire

Sunk in 1868 by the Rhymney Iron Co., who sank two shafts, each about 350ft deep to the Brithdir coal seam. On 16 January 1889 the accident reports show that seventy-six-year-old doorman Lewis Meredith was killed underground while walking along the engine plane on his way out to the shaft; he was run over. He evidently did not notice that the journey of drams was so near, as the requisite manholes were provided and there was ample space for him to have walked at the side. On 5 December 1891 the accident reports show that thirty-one-year-old collier David E. Bowen was killed underground by a stone from the roof falling on him.

In 1909 the general manager was Mr William Bowen and with a manpower of 450 miners produced around 500 tons of coal daily and about fifty repairers worked the night shift. Through its thirty-year history, it had been worked with naked lights and no significant amount of gas had been detected there. But on Friday 29 October 1909 at 4.00 a.m. twenty-seven men and boys were killed by an explosion. Thomas Williams, the banksman, was about to send an ostler down the upcast shaft and he reached for the lever that would give the all-clear to James Roberts the winding engineman. As he did so, a massive explosion vented at his feet that swept away the pit head casing and the rail-plates on which he stood. Thomas Williams and the ostler were flung violently aside, soon to be pinned down by the structures now raining upon them. Both men were injured and Thomas Williams was also badly burnt by the torrent of flame and fume that had overwhelmed him.

Another 'safe mine' had suffered a cruel blast. At this point, however, a story unfolds of daredevil courage that is unusual even in this heroic context, possibly even unique. At approximately 4.20 a.m. while the banksman and ostler were being freed, Carpenter William Evans came to the pithead. Seeing the shaft to be now out of use, and in a way that robbed the entire mine of its ventilating air, he went to the downcast and entered the black hungry maw using a rope ladder that hung at its side. At pit bottom, he found Evan Jones trapped by the foot beneath the damaged cage and he also comforted Eli Tovey who was lying injured nearby. He then climbed to the surface and persuaded two others to make the same ghastly descent with him. The three men were able to release Evan Jones and he and Eli Tovey were carried up the crazy flimsy web of string. William Evans made three such double trips before exhaustion laid him low.

Those underground who survived the blast, or were untouched by it, made for the Gilfach shaft as their escape line with clouds of blackdamp pressing hard at their heels. It was down this shaft that Mr William Bowen led his five-strong rescue party, equipped with breathing apparatus that was to prove ineffective because of its small storage capacity.

Of that group three soon fell insensible, each one carried back a presumed safe distance by the others. David Jones and Jack McCarthy, the remaining two, were now so greatly weakened that they were barely able to save themselves and their three companions William Bowen, Gomer Griffiths overman, and David Morgan fireman, were later found dead. That avenue of relief was now closed to those trapped by the blast.

At this time a party of eight had entered the mine in the manner of William Evans. Three of them, Dr Wagner Turner the mine surgeon, ex-councillor David Lewis, the undermanager at Groesfaen Colliery, and William Edwards, a contractor at Darran Colliery, were overcome soon after leaving pit bottom. Dr Turner was to make a slow painful recovery but not so the other two and death and enfeeblement bore down the little band.

The explosion at Darran Colliery on Friday 29 October 1909 claimed the lives of the following twenty-seven men and boys:

Names of casualties	Age	Occupation	Names of casualties	Age	Occupation
1. Sidney Anthony	18	labourer	12. Ambrose Jones	55	repairer
2. John Baragwenith	27	haulier	13. John Jones	43	fireman
3. William Barker	37	labourer	14. Dan McCarthy	34	collier
4. William Brown	44	collier	15. John Morgan	28	haulier
5. Daniel Cleary	33	collier	16. Lewis Morgan	25	repairer
6. Morgan Coombes	58	repairer	17. Evan Prosser	65	repairer
7. William Davies	25	haulier	18. Ernest Roberts	32	repairer
8. David Edwards	45	collier	19. John Tovey	16	collier
9. Henry Edwards	17	collier	20. Charles Vaughan	36	labourer
10. John Evans	18	collier	21. Joseph Vincent	18	collier
11. David Jenkins	56	repairer	22. James Weeks	24	collier

Rescuers who died
23. William Bowen, general manager of Bargoed Colliery, married with six children.
24. William Edwards, contractor, of Groeswen House.
25. Gomer Griffiths, overman, of Gilfach Street, Bargoed.
26. David Lewis, undermanager, of Gilfach Colliery.
27. David Morgan, fireman, of Buttrel Terrace, Fleur-De-Lys.

Deep Duffryn Colliery, Mountain Ash in 1967.

At the inquest it was held that a shot had been fired and that it had not been properly rammed home and this had ignited coal dust suspended in the atmosphere. Darran Colliery was abandoned in 1919.

Deep Duffryn Colliery, Mountain Ash, Cynon Valley, Glamorganshire

Deep Duffryn Colliery was opened in 1850 by David Williams and George Insole and later developed by John Nixon to become part of the Nixons Navigation Coal Co. and was owned by the Powell Duffryn Steam Coal Co. (PDs Poverty and Dole) prior to nationalisation on 1 January 1947. On 28 September 1868 the accident reports show that twenty-one-year-old collier Caleb Bray was killed underground by a fall of roof; on 5 January 1872 the accident reports show that thirty-six-year-old stoker Thomas Mahoney was killed by ventilator machinery; on 15 March 1873 the accident reports show that forty-seven-year-old roadman John Lucy was killed underground when he was struck by drams on an engine plane (main roadway) and on 6 September 1873 the accident reports show that thirty-year-old haulier Thomas Phillips was killed underground when he was struck by a journey of drams. Deep Duffryn Colliery was closed in September 1979 by the NCB.

Deep Navigation Colliery, Treharris, Taff Bargoed Valley, Glamorganshire

Deep Navigation Colliery was one of a number of profitable collieries owned by the Ocean Coal Co., founded by the famous David Davies of Llandinam. Originally known as Harris's Navigation, after the company's principal shareholder, who also gave his name to the village of Treharris, the pit was sunk between 1873 and 1879. At its completion, it was the deepest mine in the South Wales Coalfield by some 600ft and the downcast shaft reached the Nine-Feet coal seam at a depth of 2,280ft. Everything at Harris Navigation was bigger and better than most other pits at the time. Two years after the centenary celebrations the colliery recorded the best ever profit of £2.6 million and in the second week of May 1981 the 780 men hit a productivity record of 3 tons 1cwt per man shift. The total saleable output for the week was 9,595 tons.

On 4 February 1886 the accident reports show that thirty-nine-year-old collier Dennis Manning was killed underground by a stone falling on his head and on 31 January 1892 the accident reports show that forty-nine-year-old pitman Evan Jones was killed when he was struck by the rebound of a stone while loading rubbish in a lodge room. Deep Navigation Colliery was closed in March 1991 by British Coal.

Dinas Main Colliery, Gilfach Goch, Cwm Ogwr Valley, Glamorganshire

Dinas Main Colliery, Gilfach Goch, was sunk in 1864 by Christmas Evans, son of Evan Evans of Six Bells. On 12 December 1907 an explosion killed seven men and boys; the pit was closed and never worked again. Naked flame lights were in use at the time. During its existence the pit was acquired and became part of the larger Britannic Colliery complex.

The explosion at Dinas Main Colliery on 12 December 1907 claimed the lives of the following seven miners:

Names of casualties	Age	Occupation
1. William David	40	ripper
2. Richard Evans	33	rider
3. Watkin Evans	39	ripper
4. John Jenkins	65	roadman
5. David Miles	23	labourer
6. Nicholas White	45	ripper
7. William White	24	ripper

Dinas Main Colliery was closed on Thursday 12 December 1907.

Dinas Middle Colliery, Dinas, Rhondda Valley, Glamorganshire

In 1809 Walter Coffin bought Dinas Uchaf Farm to prospect for coal on the estate. His first level was opened to the Rhondda No.1 coal seam, which was difficult to work, and the coal was of poor quality. He then opened another level to the Rhondda No.2 coal seam and the coal was of good quality. In 1810 and 1811 he leased further mineral rights and in 1812 sank the Dinas Lower Colliery to the Rhondda No.3 coal seam, the first deep mine in the Rhondda Valley, known as Coffin's Coal. The Dinas Middle Colliery was sunk in 1832 by Walter Coffin. In 1886 a further shaft was opened by Daniel Thomas. On 1 January 1844 an explosion killed twelve men and boys, the youngest being nine years old, and was the first major explosion in the Rhondda Valley; on 13 January 1879 a further explosion killed sixty-three men and boys.

The explosion at Dinas Middle Colliery on 1 January 1844 claimed the lives of the following twelve men and boys:

Names of casualties	Age	Names of casualties	Age
1. William Harry	20	10. John Richards	14
2. David Job	14	11. Thomas Rowlands snr	61
3. Thomas Leyshon	16	12. David Rowlands jnr	9
4. David Morgan	14		
5. Lewis Morris	12	Names of injured	
6. Thomas Morris snr	48	1. Thomas Evans	
7. William Morris jnr	17	2. William Llewellyn	
8. David Phillips	22	3. William Williams	
9. Edward Powell	21		

The overman Griffith Williams had gone down the pit at approximately 4.00 a.m. with a boy, Edmund Llewellyn, son of the colliery manager Daniel Llewellyn, as his companion. The Coroner severely censured overman Griffith Williams and courteously asked the jury to return a verdict of manslaughter. This it declined to do.

Dinas Mines Rescue Team in 1912. Dinas Mines Rescue Station was opened on the 27 June 1912 with a visit by King George V and Queen Mary. The rescue station in situated 200yds from the first shaft sunk in the Rhondda Valley by Walter Coffin. The building was built by contractors Messrs Niblett & Davies of Cardiff at a cost of £3,448 17s 3d.

Just before midnight on 13 January 1879 a violent blast shook the houses nearby and all the residents rushed to the top of the smoking pit (the author's father was born 100 yards from the top of the pit). By midnight all had died and it was all over in one brief moment in time.

The explosion at Dinas Middle Colliery on Monday 13 January 1879 at 11.45 p.m. claimed the lives of the following sixty-three men and boys:

Names of casualties	Age	Occupation	Names of casualties	Age	Occupation
1. Jas. Bowen	45	repairer or labourer	10. Robert Emery	29	repairer or labourer
2. Robert Chubb	30	timberman	11. Joseph Evans	18	haulier
3. William Cross	31	timberman	12. William Evans	27	repairer or labourer
4. Evan Davies	52	lamp station	13. John Griffiths	21	repairer or labourer
5. Edward Davies	20	repairer or labourer			
6. Daniel Dunn	34	haulier	14. John Griffiths	30	hitcher
7. Daniel Dunworth	30	cutting top	15. William Griffiths	50	repairer or labourer
8. Jas. Edwards	17	haulier	16. Jas. Harris	33	cutting bottom
9. John Edwards	20	haulier			

Names of casualties	Age	Occupation	Names of casualties	Age	Occupation
17. John Hawkins	48	repairer or labourer	38. Samuel Pryor	29	repairer or labourer
18. Henry Hayter	22	cutting top	39. David Rees	28	repairer or labourer
§9. Richard Howells	31	repairer or labourer	40. Edward Rees	19	haulier
20. David Hughes	34	repairer or labourer	41. Thomas Rees	21	repairer or labourer
21. Thomas Hughes	30	repairer or labourer	42. Thomas Richards	26	cutting bottom
22. David Jenkins	27	repairer or labourer	43. William Richards	18	repairer or labourer
23. Evan Jenkins	16	haulier	44. Thomas Roberts	59	repairer or labourer
24. John Jenkins	30	repairer or labourer	45. William Roberts	28	haulier
25. Thomas Jenkin	40	cutting bottom	46. John Roomsville	39	repairer
26. William Jenkins	35	hitcher	47. Sam Roomsville	37	repairer or labourer
27. Evan John	34	cutting top	48. James Rossin	26	repairer or labourer
28. William Jones	26	timberman	49. Daniel Smith	49	cutting top
29. River Jordon	51	repairer or labourer	50. Edward Sullivan	30	cutting bottom
30. John Landregan	26	repairer or labourer	51. George Sutton	35	labourer
31. John Lewis	49	repairer or labourer	52. Henry Taylor	30	labourer
32. William Lloyd	36	night fireman	53. David Thomas	34	haulier
33. Isaac Martin	24	repairer or labourer	54. Elisha Upjohn	51	repairer
34. Charles Meade	22	repairer or labourer	55. Thomas Watkins	34	night fireman
35. Frank Moore	26	repairer or labourer	56. Charles Westlake	52	labourer
36. Daniel Morley	18	haulier	57. Charles Wheadon	24	labourer
37. Charles Penny	34	timberman	58. Oct Wheadon	40	labourer
			59. Henry Williams	28	repairer
			60. Lewis Williams	37	haulier
			61. Stephen Williams	37	timberman
			62. William Williams	28	labourer
			63. William Williams	22	haulier

On 8 November 1872 the accident reports show that twenty-one-year-old R. Morgan was killed underground by a fall of stone; on 22 October 1874 the accident reports show that eighteen-year-old D. Thomas was killed underground by falling under drams; on 15 June 1875 the accident reports show that collier T.H. Thomas was killed underground by a journey of drams and on 16 August 1875 the accident reports show that haulier John Lewis was killed underground by a journey of drams. On 13 January 2004 Thomas and Vivian Chubb, the great-grandsons of Robert Chubb who died in the explosion on 13 January 1879, attended a memorial ceremony at Trealaw Cemetery. Thomas Chubb said, 'When the rescue party recovered my great-grandfather's body from the underground workings three years after the explosion, it was brought to the surface in a coal dram and finally laid to rest'. Dinas Middle Colliery was closed in 1893.

Dowlais Colliery, Near Merthyr Tydfil, Taff Vale, Glamorganshire

Dowlais Colliery was opened by the Dowlais Iron Co. in 1853. On 9 February 1853 the accident reports show that twenty-eight-year-old labourer T. Mahoney was killed underground by a journey of drams; on 30 November 1853 the accident reports show that fifty-five-year-old labourer William Roberts was killed when he was run over on the railway; on 8 February 1860 the accident reports show that collier Tom Davies was killed underground by a fall of coal; on 8 August 1860 the accident reports show that thirty-two-year-old collier Tom. Griffiths was killed underground by a fall of roof and on 15 February 1872 the accident reports show that sixteen-year-old D. Morgans was killed underground. Dowlais Colliery was abandoned in 1922.

Duffryn Colliery, Cwmbach, Cynon Valley, Glamorganshire

Duffryn Colliery, Cwmbach, was sunk in 1843 and was owned by Mr Thomas Powell. At approximately 11.00 a.m. on Saturday 1 August 1845 there came a dreadful explosion that shook every house in the vicinity and cost the lives of twenty-eight men and boys. The explosion was

The first ambulance used by Dowlais Colliery, Merthyr Tydfil, Taff Vale, Glamorganshire in 1912. In 1886 a Royal Commission recommended the establishment of mines rescue stations, Crumlin and Aberaman in 1908, New Tredegar 1910. They did not become widespread until the Coal Mines Act of 1911 made them compulsory.

confined to one underground heading in the mine. Three pit ponies were also killed and the bodies of some of the victims could not be brought up the pit until late on Monday 3 August.

The explosion at Duffryn Colliery on 1 August 1845 claimed the lives of the following twenty-eight men and boys:

Names of casualties	Age	Marital status	Names of casualties	Age	Marital status
1. Howell John David	20	single	15. John Jones	17	single
2. Thomas Davies	78		16. Evan Lewis	19	single
3. John Edwards	35	married	17. William Llewellyn	18	single
4. William Edwards	23	single	18. David Morgan	20	single
5. David Evans	9	single	19. Richard Morris	30	single
6. John Evans	22	single	20. Joseph Phillips	19	single
7. Nicholas Evans	14	single	21. Thomas Rees	23	single
8. Thomas Evans	41	married	22. Thomas Smith	19	single
9. William Evans	31	married	23. George Thomas	33	single
10. James James	23	single	24. James Thomas	42	married
11. David Jenkins	37	single	25. David Thomas	10	single
12. David Jones	32	married	26. Evan Thomas	14	single
13. David Jones	27	married	27. Rees Williams	24	single
14. John Jones	17	single	28. Howell Williams	28	single

The jury returned a verdict of accidental death.

On 16 March 1885 the accident reports show that fifteen-year-old collier W.H. Lewis was injured underground by a fall of stone and died from his injuries; on 6 March 1886 and 12 September 1885 the accident reports show that sixty-year-old engineman Thomas Kellow Hawkes was injured on the colliery surface when he slipped while descending some steps from the engine-house and was considerable shaken. He died on 14 August 1886, according to the verdict of the Coroner's jury, from the effects thereof. The company's officials do not share in that opinion. Duffryn Colliery was closed in 1886.

Elba Colliery, Gowerton, Glamorganshire

Elba Colliery was opened by Wright, Butler & Co. in 1851. On 18 April 1889 the accident reports show that twenty-six-year-old collier David Thomas was killed underground by a fall of roof 9ft x 3ft x 2ft at the face of a level going alongside a fault. The coal was only 18ins in thickness next to the fault and 6ft on the opposite side of the level. 2ft 6ins of roof had been ripped down on the low side to within 2ft 6ins of the face of coal. There were no pit props below the rippings which fell. The accident happened in the Six-Feet coal seam. The pillar stall system was in use. The pillar and stall is a system of working in which the deposit is in the first working cut into blocks or pillars, which are subsequently removed in the second working.

On 27 January 1905 an explosion killed ten men and boys at Elba Colliery which was owned by Baldwin & Co. who were also owners of Gowerton Steelworks, who used all the coal produced by the colliery. The explosion occurred in the Six-Feet coal seam in the No.7 level at the far end of the main roadway. The ignition came near the end of the shift, when they were so tired and weary from toiling, but one man who survived the explosion was Mr Nurse. He was later to say, 'I lost myself for some time'; when his senses returned he was stumbling in the smoky blackness. Some of the victims had been stripped bare by the blast.

The explosion at Elba Colliery on 27 January 1905 near the end of the working shift claimed the lives of the following ten men and boys:

Names of casualties	Age	Occupation	Names of casualties	Age	Occupation
1. William Bowen	18	collier	6. Thomas Pratt	18	collier
2. Daniel Davies	26	collier	7. David John Rees	21	trammer
3. William Davies	60	collier	8. Edward Rees	26	collier
4. William Henry Morgan	20	trammer	9. George Rees	23	trammer
5. Alexander Ogilvie	20	trammer	10. George Williams	14	doorboy

Seriously injured
1. Thomas Bevan
2. Robert Davies
3. David Edwards
4. John Long
5. David Ogilvie

Elba Colliery was closed in 1921.

Elliot Colliery, New Tredegar, Rhymney Valley, Glamorganshire

Elliot Colliery opened in 1885 and was named after Sir George Elliot, one of the directors of the Powell Duffryn Steam Coal Co. On 7 June 1884 the accident reports show that twenty-one-year-old sinker Gwilym Williams was killed when he was walling while sinking Elliot Pit when a three-cornered stone fell on him; on 30 August 1884 the accident reports show that forty-five-year-old engineman William Morgan was killed when he was knocked off a staging in the shaft and fell to the bottom of the pit; on 26 April 1890 the accident reports show that twenty-six-year-old collier Phillip James was killed underground by a fall of roof. He was engaged securing the place with props; on 14 August 1890 the reports show that thirty-year-old collier John Bale was killed underground by a fall of coal which he was holing. He had holed the coal with sprags set; these he knocked out, and as the coal did not fall, he without setting new sprags resumed holing and within a few minutes it dropped on him; on 14 August 1890 the accident reports show that twenty-two-year-old collier D. Wilkins was killed underground by a fall of roof near the face. The roof at his place of work was very weak and was liable to fall without warning. The only safeguard was the use of extra timber and on 14 August 1890 the reports show that forty-eight-year-old heading man John Williams was killed underground by a fall of roof. Elliot Colliery was closed in April 1967 by the NCB.

Ferndale Colliery, Rhondda Valley, Glamorganshire

Almost all the population was lodged in houses built of wood, like American log-huts. When sinking had commenced at Ferndale in 1857, there were but a few farmhouses in the locality:

Blaenllechau and Nant-dyrys in the parish of Llanwynno, Ffaldau in the parish of Aberdare, Duffryn Sarfwch and Rhondda Fechan in the parish of Ystradyfodwg. Immediately the steam coal seams were won, advertisements appeared in the South Wales press offering work under good conditions at Ferndale. At first, the difficulty of accommodating the workers and their families was a serious one. The original sinkers, about forty in number, had been housed as one community in a single dwelling house 'Y Lluest', while the first miners and their families were accommodated in a large number of wooden huts called the 'Barracks'. Indeed, the *Times* reporter who visited Ferndale in November 1867 described how 'almost all the population of 800 was lodged in houses crudely built of wood, like American log huts'. It was in the 1870s, when large numbers migrated into the district, that the huts were taken down and long terraces of stone houses were built by the colliery company to give shelter to this rapidly growing population. Delta Davies, the first cashier of David Davis and Sons, changed the name Glynrhedynog to Ferndale in 1862.

At the Ferndale No.1 Pit output grew at an astonishing rate from 11,138 tons in 1864 to 94,691 tons in 1868. The brothers David Davis and Lewis Davis (previously in charge of the sales department at Cardiff) became partners with their father in 1866 and subsequently the firm was known as 'David Davis and Sons'. On the sudden death of David Davis Senior on 20 May 1866, the control of the firm fell to the two sons. They were faced immediately with major crises on the occasion of two serious explosions, the first on 8 November 1867 with a loss of life of 178 and such grim statistics were put into context by one news correspondent who wrote, 'I doubt if any previous accident recorded in the annals of coal mining can have proved fatal to so large a proportion of the population of a district as this one. There are not more than two houses in the village that will not have to take on one or more dead bodies in the place of the living man or boy, which left there'.

The second explosion was on 10 June 1869 when fifty-three miners were killed and at the resumption of the inquest on 1 July, the Coroner addressed the jury:

> Again you have been summoned away from your homes and domestic duties, to discharge a most serious and important duty; another serious and appalling calamity has occurred in this district and caused grief and dismay to many households. It becomes our duty to investigate the circumstances and ascertain as far as possible the origin of the unfortunate occurrence.

Over the following days the court heard technical evidence presented by various pit officials. It was recorded that a fall had occurred on the day prior to the explosion. Several pockets of gas had been noted and marked by the fireman within the Duffryn area. Barometrical readings and ventilation information were also provided. During the second day of the hearing, the Coroner was informed that another body had been recovered, bringing the total of dead recovered to forty-nine. The enquiry failed to reveal the exact cause of the explosion despite volumes of testimony from dozens of witnesses. The general consensus however was that gross negligence and lack of discipline by the general manager had contributed to most of the events that led up to the explosion and the verdict of the jury stated: 'We find that the deceased came to their death from an explosion of firedamp in the Ferndale Colliery, on the 10 June last; but we have not sufficient evidence to satisfy us as to where it arose'. In their summing up they added:

> We regret that we should have to investigate another explosion in this colliery so soon after the terrible catastrophe of 1867. We regret also that the suggestions of the jury on that occasion have not all been fully carried out by the manager and other officers of the pit.

These disasters, in such rapid succession, threatened ruin to the mining enterprise. For a time, Ferndale had a bad name as a bad place and the shadow of death seemed to rest over the valley.

Two miners prepared for work at Ferndale Colliery in 1907. The naked flame safety lamp was in use. The young miner has a naked flame safety lamp in his right hand, a Tommy Box (food box) under his left arm and he is also carrying a 3pt drinking water Jack in his left hand.

People were drifting away and many prophesied that getting men to work there again would be difficult, if not impossible. In his report on the explosion of 1867, HM Inspector, Thomas Wales, described Ferndale No.1 Pit as 'one of the best ventilated and best managed pits under my supervision'. But Lewis Davis (1829-1888), the second founder of the Ferndale enterprise, decided to improve ventilation further by opening a new shaft Ferndale No.2 Pit in 1870 about a mile higher up the valley. The new venture was so successful that, in the flourishing seventies, the mineral taking was extended and several new shafts were opened. On 3 May 1890, the Ferndale concern became a limited company, which immediately purchased the Bodringallt Colliery in the Rhondda Fawr (subsequently Ferndale No.3 Pit). Bodringallt Colliery was opened in 1864 by Warner, Simpson and Co., Ystrad and by vesting date 1 January 1947 was retained for ventilation. Bodringallt Colliery closed in 1959. By 1914, the Ferndale mineral property embraced all the seams lying under a surface area of between six and seven square miles, covering one continuous coal-taking extending from the Rhondda Fach to the Rhondda Fawr, with their northern boundary near Mardy Colliery and their southern boundary at Tylorstown worked by nine winding shafts. In the same year 5,654 men were employed, producing an output of 1,750,000 tons. From the small beginnings of 1862 had grown one of the major colliery enterprises in the South Wales Coalfield. The unveiling of the Memorial for the Ferndale Collieries took place on Friday 15 July 1988 in memory of the 178 miners who lost their lives on 8 November 1867 and the fifty-three miners who lost their lives on 10 June 1869 at Ferndale No.1 Pit. Buried beneath the memorial in a steel 'time capsule' is a scroll inscribed with all the names of the 231 miners who died in the Ferndale Colliery explosions.

Ferndale No.1 and No.5 Colliery in 1904. In August 1862, the first load of steam coal was sent from Ferndale to Cardiff and the industrial era of the Rhondda Fach had begun. The colliery was owned by the Powell Duffryn Steam Coal Co. prior to nationalisation in 1947. Ferndale No.1 and No.5 Colliery was closed on 29 August 1959 by the NCB.

The explosion at Ferndale Colliery on 10 June 1869 claimed the lives of the following fifty-three men and boys:

Names of casualties	Age	Marital status
1. George Allen	33	single
2. George Chamberlain	29	single
3. Daniel Davies		
4. Edmund Davies		
5. John Davies	21	single
6. Samuel Davies	28	single
7. Abel Dore	24	single
8. John Edwards	32	married
9. Thomas Elliott	40	married
10. Henry Exell		
11. Joseph Exell		
12. James Griffiths		
13. William Hughes		
14. David Jones	24	single
15. David Jones	24	single
16. James Jones	50	married
17. Richard Jones		
18. John Jones	21	single
19. Morgan Jones snr		married

20. Morgan Jones jnr	13	single
21. Morgan Jones	14	single
22. Thomas Jones	28	married
23. Thomas Jones	14	single
24. Thomas Jones	24	married
25. William Jones	30	married
26 William Llewellyn	17	single
27. Abraham Mathews	43	single
28. Jacob Mathews	48	married
29. John Mathews	28	single
30. William Mathews		
31. John Morgan	22	single
32. James Morgan	34	married
33. James Morris		
34. Richard L. Morris	23	single
35. James Nash	32	married
36. Evan Phillips	43	single
37. Thomas Price		
38. John Price	50	married
39. Evan Richards	48	married
40. Windsor Roderick	23	single
41. David Samuel	59	married
42. Samuel Straide		
43. Charles Taylor	43	married
44. George B. Thomas	31	married
45. Thomas Thomas	34	single
46. Thomas Thomas	27	single
47. Thomas Thomas	22	single
48. John Thomas	23	married

The unveiling of the Memorial for the Ferndale Collieries on Friday 15 July 1988. In memory of the 178 miners who lost their lives on 8 November 1867 and the fifty-three miners who lost their lives on 10 June 1869 at Ferndale No.1 Pit. Buried beneath the memorial in a steel 'time capsule' is a scroll inscribed with all the names of the 231 miners who died in the Ferndale Colliery explosions.

49. Edward Waddleton	30	married
50. Bendigo Weeks	24	single
51. James Wilkins	13	single
52. Evan Williams	25	single
53. David Williams	21	single

Ferndale No.1 and No.5 Colliery was closed on Saturday 29 August 1959 by the NCB.

Gelli Colliery, Gelli, Rhondda Valley, Glamorganshire

Gelli Colliery was sunk in 1877 by Edmund Thomas. Five miners were killed when an explosion occurred at 7.30 a.m. on 21 August 1883. The colliery was acquired by the NCB in 1947.

The explosion at Gelli Colliery on Tuesday 21 August 1883 claimed the following five miners' lives:

Names of casualties	Age	Occupation
1. Mr John Chubb	44	undermanager
2. John Jones	46	collier
3. John Lewis	46	collier
4. David Thomas	32	collier
5. Thomas Woodcliff	26	collier

Gelli Colliery was closed in January 1962 by the NCB.

Gethin Colliery, Near Merthyr Tydfil, Taff Vale, Glamorganshire

And where is Gethin? Every collier knew it and a large proportion of those who were not colliers. It was within a few miles of Cyfarthfa and was opened in 1848. But just as wars and tragedies bring insignificant places to light of day so happened to Gethin – the name of which means harsh and cruel, quite a coincidence when we consider the sad disasters that occurred there.

The first explosion took place on 16 February 1862 and the loss of life on that occasion was forty-seven miners. There were thirty-nine widows and mothers left destitute, and a whole host of children. The calamity was a novel one for the English world, and the news aroused the sympathy of all classes; the richest man and the poorest servant girl sent their aid, and the total fund gathered amounted to £6,000. Let us not forget the Revd John Griffith who did his part in touching the nation's heart. This fund met all requirements well and a committee was formed, with Mr Thomas Stephens of Merthyr as secretary, carried out the wishes of the subscribers to the letter. Through emigration, death, or re-marriage the number of widows had been drastically reduced. In fact, there were only ten persons on the fund and these received collectively £4 6s 0d per week. The money was first invested in the India Five per Cents, then as money became of less value, in the Four per Cents and at last in The Three-and-a-Half per Cents.

A further explosion in 1865 killed thirty-five miners. The explosion at Gethin Colliery on Wednesday 20 December 1865 at 8.00 a.m. claimed the lives of the following men and boys:

Names of casualties	Age	Marital status
1. David Beddoe	49	married
2. Thomas Bowen	42	married
3. John Daniel	47	married
4. David Davies	18	single
5. Rees Davies	11	single
6. Rees Davies	75	married
7. David Ellis	41	married
8. Griffith Ellis	48	married
9. Samuel Harris	28	married
10. John James	22	single
11. Harding Lewis	35	married
12. Henry Lewis	13	single
13. John Lewis	16	single
14. David Luke	12	single
15. John Luke	34	married
16. Griff Morgan	42	married
17. John Morgan	33	married
18. John Morgan	21	married
19. Joseph Morgan	23	single
21. Thomas Morgan	35	married
22. William Morris	42	married
23 John Phelps	13	single
24. Joseph Rees	29	married
25. Vavasour Rees	51	married
26. William Rees	16	single
27. Alexander Richards	23	single
28. Wycliffe Bill Stephens	15	single
29. Daniel Price Thomas	20	married
30. David Thomas	24	married
31. James Thomas	22	single
32. Lewis Price Thomas	25	single
33. Morgan Thomas	16	single
34. Morgan Thomas	16	single
35. Roderick Thomas	20	single

Gethin Colliery was abandoned on Friday 21 July 1893.

Hafod Colliery, Trehafod, Rhondda Valley, Glamorganshire

David and John Thomas leased the mineral rights of Hafod Fach and Nyth Bran Farm and opened the Hafod Colliery in 1850. The Coed Cae No.1 and No.2 were sunk in 1850, the Bertie in 1880

Left: The Hafod Colliery in 1920.

Above: International Colliery, Blaengarw, Garw Valley, in 1937.

and the Trefor in 1890. From 1870, all the Lewis Merthyr Colliery operations belonged to William Thomas Lewis, later Lord Merthyr. Lewis Merthyr Colliery was formed from six shafts into the same workings. In 1913 the manpower in the Hafod was 1,130. In 1929 they were taken over by the Powell Duffryn Steam Coal Co., who remained owners until nationalisation in 1947. The site now has given birth to the Rhondda Heritage Park for visitors.

On 11 May 1860 the accident reports show that thirty-year-old collier Samuel Phillips was killed underground by a fall of stone (a bed) from the roof; on 22 March 1873 the accident reports show that twenty-four-year-old collier William Jones was killed underground by a fall of roof; on 3 March 1874 the accident reports show that collier D. Morgan was killed underground by a fall of roof; on 27 May 1884 the accident reports show that collier D. Morgan was also killed underground by a fall of roof; on 12 June 1886 fifty-two-year-old haulier Thomas Evans was killed on the colliery surface when he fell under a dram and on 22 April 1891 twenty-four-year-old night haulier William Beynon was killed underground by hitching his horse to a dram and he missed the iron and it fell, causing the horse to become restive and the deceased fell against the dram. He was, apparently, only slightly injured, but inflammation of the brain supervened and he died on 11 May 1891. Hafod No.2 Colliery ceased producing coal in 1930 and the Hafod No.1 Colliery in 1933.

Hendreladais Colliery, Near Ystradgynlais, Swansea Valley, Glamorganshire

Hendreladais Colliery was opened by Ynyscedwyn Iron Co. in 1850. On 16 November 1853 the accident reports show that fifteen-year-old collier Rees Thomas was killed underground when a stone fell from the roof; on 18 December 1853 the accident reports show that twenty-three-year-old miner John Thomas was killed underground by a fall of roof whilst escaping and on 17 October 1874 the accident reports show that colliers S. Jones and H. Watkin were killed underground by gunpowder igniting whilst the deceased and two others were ramming a hole. Hendreladais Colliery was closed in 1919.

Hollybush Colliery, Near Hollybush, Sirhowy Valley, Monmouthshire

Hollybush Colliery was opened in 1870 by E.D. Williams. On 7 November 1884 the accident reports show that thirty-one-year-old collier John Davies was killed underground by a fall of roof. He was working in a stall with his father, everything appeared safe, when a fall occurred, which killed him and seriously injured his father. Hollybush Colliery was closed in 1921.

Hook Colliery, Haverfordwest, Pembrokeshire

Hook Colliery was opened by the Hook Colliery Co. in 1875 to replace such pits as Green, New Aurora, Old Aurora and West Park which was replaced by the Margaret Pit in 1910. The pits were shallow and sunk to a depth of 60–80 yards to work the Timber Vein coal seam. On 2 October 1875 the accident reports show that a pit overman was killed by falling down the air pit when the rope broke; on 3 April 1860 the accident reports show that fifteen-year-old trammer (trammers were boys or girls who pushed drams filled with seven hundredweights of coal in the nineteenth century) John Heir was killed when a bucket fell down the shaft from the top and on 23 November 1892 the accident reports show that thirty-two-year-old collier William Phillips was killed underground by a fall of roof at the face while he was finishing the lagging above a pair of timbers. Hook Colliery was closed on Friday 23 April 1948 by the NCB.

International Colliery, Garw Valley, Glamorganshire

International Colliery, Blaengarw, Garw Valley. International Colliery, No.1 Downcast Shaft height above OD was 737ft. Site 850 yards N 38° W of Mount Zion church, Blaengarw. Deepening to 1,436ft 9ins. No.2 Upcast Shaft height above OD was 739ft. Site 850 yards N 41 degrees W of Mount Zion church, Blaengarw. International Colliery was opened in 1883 by the International Coal Co. Ltd. In 1928 it was owned by Glenavon Garw Collieries Ltd, in 1937 the Ocean Coal Co., Ocean and United National Co. and the NCB. The colliery consisted of two shafts, a level, with a third shaft being sunk in 1910; the level closed in 1923. It was later linked with the Garw Colliery. In 1889 the colliery employed 916 miners.

On 19 March 1892 the accident reports show that twenty-six-year-old haulier John Lewis was killed underground by a fall of roof at the road end which was not timbered; at 6.50 p.m. on 24 July 1895 the accident reports show that eighteen-year-old haulier Thomas Williams was killed when he fell from the Two-Feet-Nine landing to the Six-Feet coal seam. He had just got out of the cage when he fell backwards into the pit where there was a space of 15ins wide to allow air to pass down to the Six-Feet coal seam; at 9.00 a.m. on 27 June 1895 the accident reports show that forty-eight-year-old haulier David Jones was killed underground when he was run over by an empty journey of drams while he was oiling the sheaves and rollers. He was acting as roadman for that day; on 7 December 1897 the accident reports show that forty-two-year-old labourer Charles Comely was killed on the colliery surface when he was run over by a dram of rubbish as he was crossing a dramway on his way to the lamp room; on 28 December 1898 the accident reports show that twenty-six-year-old rider William Edwards was killed underground while he was filling loose coal off a main road; he attacked the pillar on the side, when the clift above which was 4ft x 15ins x 15ins fell upon him; and on 13 September 1889 the accident reports show that nineteen-year-old collier Robert Martin was injured underground at the face by a strong clift 10ft x 35ins x 18ins thick which was not propped He died on 23 September 1889. The fireman (deputy) told the deceased an hour previous to set a row of props and a cog. International Colliery was closed on Saturday 4 November 1967 by the NCB.

International Anthracite Colliery, Abercrâf, Swansea Valley, Breconshire

International Anthracite Colliery was opened by the French Anthracite Co. in 1894. It was also worked by International Anthracite Co. At 5.00 p.m. on 9 August 1894 the accident reports show that thirty-seven-year-old furnaceman Evan James was killed underground by an explosion of gas; on 29 November 1897 the accident reports show that twenty-three-year-old collier James Jones was injured underground at the face. He died on 21 December 1897 from his injuries by the fall of a small stone while clearing some fallen stones on entering his place of work and on 17 June 1897 the accident reports show that twenty-four-year-old rider (a rider is a journey of drams attendant responsible for the safe movement of a journey) James Jones was killed underground when he fell off a journey of drams at the mouth of a slant at a curve; he was riding in front. International Anthracite Colliery was closed in January 1947 by the NCB.

Jones's Pit, Ynyshir, Rhondda Valley, Glamorganshire

Jones's Pit height above Ordinance Datum 388ft. 6in ST 09 S.E. Glam 27 NE. Site 600 yards S.2* E of Ynyshir church. National Grid ref. 02559626. This Ynyshir Colliery, locally known as Jones's Pit, was sunk by Messrs Shepherd and Evans in 1849 and seven years later it was purchased by Francis Crawshay to supply coal for his tinplate works at Treforest, the colliery employing about 100 men. In 1873 the colliery was owned by Thomas Jones of Maindy House, Ynyshir. The shaft was 198ft deep and the colliery worked the Rhondda No.2 coal seam at a section of 2ft 6ins to 3ft, which supplied their own coking ovens. On Saturday 12 May 1877 there was an explosion. At midday three men, John Howell, John Hopkins and Abraham Dodds, were driving a windway between the two shafts. They were drilling ahead and had holed into the passageway on the other side. Gas came through the holes made by the drills and burned in their Davy lamps. The lamps became hotter and hotter and Dodd suggested it was time to put them out. Hopkins assured him that there was no danger as he had been in the other passageway and it did not contain a dangerous quantity of gas. When the hole had been enlarged, Dodd put his head and arms through. At that moment there was a lurid flash and the explosion hurled Dodd back many yards. He felt his arms frying. Abraham Dodd lived in a cottage by the riverside at Ferndale; he suffered great pain, as his face, arms and body looked like cooked meat. Isaac Pride took part in the final, most dangerous part of the rescue at Tynewydd Colliery with Abraham Dodd and if any man deserved to be recognised that man was Dodd. Why does his name not appear? One can only guess at the explanation. Perhaps someone who reads these words may be in a position to clear the matter finally. It would give pleasure to another generation of Rhondda people to honour a man whose deeds were as great as those who were honoured by the Queen.

The Forest Fach coal seam was at a depth of 149ft 11ins with a thickness of 10ins and the Rhondda No.2 coal seam at a depth of 174ft with a thickness of 2ft 10ins. On 18 April 1888 the accident reports show that eighteen-year-old collier George Gardner was killed underground by a fall of roof on the gob side of a road while he was drawing back pillars in the Rhondda No.2 coal seam; on 27 April 1899 the accident reports show that forty-eight-year-old collier William Ash was injured underground when he was unlawfully riding a dram containing two oil casks. He died on 27 October 1899 and on 1 September 1899 the accident reports show that eighteen-year-old labourer J. Pritchard was killed on the colliery surface when he was assisting to shift wagons at the screens. He was crushed between the draw-bars, probably as he was detaching the horse's chain. Jones's Pit was closed in 1909.

Kay's Slope, Blaenavon, Afon Lwyd Valley, Monmouthshire

Kay's Slope was opened in 1865. A slope is a tunnel driven at a gradient through strata and seams into the required seam, normally at a downward inclination to connect underground workings with the surface, for the transportation of coal and supplies etc. (on rails for drams). The coal was then mined without having to sink a shaft. On 9 December 1885 twenty-one-year-old collier William Briggs was fatally injured; on 8 January 1889 twenty-six-year-old haulier Henry Gibbs was killed underground by a fall of roof, stone and timber in consequence of a dram getting derailed at a turn and knocking out a prop etc; on 16 February 1899 the accident reports show that fifty-nine-year-old collier John Jones was fatally injured; on 28 February 1901 the accident reports show that fifteen-year-old labourer William Amos and twenty-three-year-old mason William Henry Roberts were killed underground by an explosion of firedamp at a naked light. They were engaged in walling a staple pit from the new vein to the lower coal seams and had got to within about 4 yards from the top. Gas accumulated under the scaffolding, owing to no provision having been made for ventilation, and ignited at the naked lights which they were using; on 25 January 1911 twenty-six-year-old collier T.J. Richards was fatally injured; on 21 August 1911 the accident reports show that seventeen-year-old repairer J.A. Edmunds was fatally injured; on 7 March 1913 the accident reports show that fifty-five-year-old William Morgan was fatally injured; on 7 August 1913 the accident reports show that fifty-nine-year-old ostler (an ostler is a horse attendant who works in underground stables) Charles Young was fatally injured and on 30 November 1913 forty-four-year-old labourer John Mogford was fatally injured. Kay's Slope was closed on Sunday 1 January 1961 by the NCB.

Kilgetty Colliery, Kilgetty, Pembrokeshire

Kilgetty Colliery was sunk in the early nineteenth century; it was sunk to supply the Stepaside Iron Works. On 6 January 1860 the accident reports show that a thirteen-year-old boy was killed underground by a fall of stone at the entrance to a stall and on 31 July 1886 the accident reports show that seventy-year-old William Stephens was killed by being caught by the cage when entering after signalling it away. He was brought to the surface suspended by the neck between the shoe and guide rod. One leg was resting in the cage. Kilgetty Colliery was closed in 1939.

Killan Colliery, Gowerton, Swansea, Glamorganshire

Killan Colliery was opened by the Killan Colliery Co. Ltd in 1900. On 31 August 1906 forty-three-year-old collier William Davies was fatally injured; on 3 December 1908 twenty-five-year-old trammer Thomas Phillip Benyon was fatally injured; on 18 January 1908 the accident reports show that seventeen-year-old incline hitcher Walter Davies was fatally injured; on 10 November 1909 sixteen-year-old assistant pumpsman Sydney Rees Morgan was fatally injured; on 19 January 1910 thirty-seven-year-old Thomas Parry was fatally injured and on 21 January 1910 sixteen-year-old collier John Bennett was fatally injured. Killan Colliery was closed on Saturday 8 August 1925.

Kille Colliery, Llanelli, Carmarthenshire

Kille Colliery was opened by C.W.M. Lewis in 1870. On 8 May 1875 the accident reports show that forty-three-year-old collier Simon James was killed underground by a shot going off whilst engaged in unramming a hole which had missed fired. In doing so, there was a violation of No.8 General Rule. Kille Colliery was closed in 1901.

Llan Colliery, Pentyrch, Glamorganshire

Llan Colliery was opened in the mid-1850s by T.W. Booker & Co. On 2 September 1872 the accident reports show that twenty-eight-year-old collier Isaac Morgan was killed underground by a fall of stone. On 6 December 1875 an explosion killed twelve men and boys.

The explosion at Llan Colliery on Wednesday 6 December 1875 claimed the lives of the following men and boys:

Names of casualties	Occupation
1. Daniel Evans	collier
2. William Peters	collier
3. Abraham Phillips	collier
4. John Pritchard	collier
5. Moses Llewellyn	collier
6. Thomas Llewellyn	collier
7. Thomas Llewellyn jnr	collier
8. William Llewellyn snr	collier
9. David Rees	collier
10. Henry Sant	collier
11. Robert Taylor	collier
12. John Thomas	collier

Names of injured	Occupation
1. Evan Davies	collier
2. Shadrach Davies	collier
3. Samuel Evans	collier
4. John Flym	collier
5. William Harding	collier
6. Abraham Williams	collier

Llan Colliery was abandoned in September 1913.

Llanerch Colliery, Near Pontypool, Afon Lwyd Valley, Monmouthshire

Llanerch Colliery was opened in 1858 by the Ebbw Vale Steel, Iron & Coal Co. Edward Jones, the managing director of the mine, by letter dated 5 December 1889, stated, 'At present we think the colliery is thoroughly well ventilated and safe to work with naked lights'. By adding his signature to this letter, Edward Jones effectively signed the death warrant of 176 men and boys as subsequently an explosion of firedamp at naked lights occurred in the No.4 heading off Cooke's slope.

The explosion at Llanerch Colliery on Thursday 6 February 1890 at approximately 8.30 a.m. claimed the lives of the following 176 men and boys:

Names of casualties	Age	Occupation
1. James Adams	36	face worker
2. William Allsopp	54	face worker
3. George Ashman	19	face worker
4. Thomas Ashman	21	face worker
5. William Ashman	17	face worker
6. William Bailey	15	doorboy
7. William J. Bayliss	21	face worker
8. John Beard	63	hitcher
9 Joseph Bevan	37	face worker
10. A. W. Bingham	15	face worker
11. Frederick Bridges	17	face worker
12. Lewis Bridges	29	face worker
13. Mark Bridges	55	face worker
14. William Bridges	19	face worker
15. James Bright	14	face worker
16. Samuel F. Bright	12	face worker
17. David Brimble	12	face worker
18. Oliver Brimble	15	face worker
19. William Brimble	17	face worker
20. Albert Bryant	34	haulier
21. John Carey	31	face worker
22, Gabriel Carpenter	47	face worker
23. Jesse Carpenter	15	face worker
24. James Cook	31	face worker

25. John Cook	37	face worker
26. Daniel Davies	24	face worker
27. E. Charles Davies	14	face worker
28. Edward Davies	54	face worker
29. George Davies	37	face worker
30. John Davies	34	face worker
31. William Davies	45	face worker
32. William Davies	14	doorboy
33. William Dobbs	24	face worker
34. John Downs	32	engineman
35. James Driscoll	52	haulier
36. John Edwards	20	face worker
37. Robert Edwards	15	face worker
38. John Evans	12	face worker
39. Thomas Filer	28	haulier
40. William Finn	17	face worker
41. Robert Furber	18	repairer
42. John Gauntlett	55	face worker
43. Joseph George	13	face worker
44. William George	34	face worker
45. William J. Godwin	13	face worker
46. Richard Gough	60	face worker
47. James Greasley	23	face worker
48. Samuel Greasley	37	face worker
49. Thomas Greasley	19	face worker
50. William Gullick	25	face worker
51. Charles Gwilym	14	doorboy
52. William Harper	28	face worker
53. William Hayes	19	face worker
54. Henry Hillier	31	face worker
55. Henry Hoare	17	face worker
56. John Hoskins	39	face worker
57. David Howells	13	face worker
58. Henry Howells	15	face worker
59. John Howells	17	face worker
60. Joseph Howells	35	face worker
61. Joseph Howells	12	face worker
62. David Hughes	14	face worker
63. Daniel Ivory	21	face worker
64. Robert Ivory	26	face worker
65. Azariah Jeremiah	57	repairer
66. George James	53	repairer
67. James James	13	face worker
68. James 'Lago' James	60	repairer
69. John James	44	face worker
70. Samuel James	19	face worker
71. Thomas James	20	face worker
72. Thomas James	14	face worker

73. Albert Jones	14	face worker
74. David Jones	14	face worker
75. Edward Jones	60	undermanager
76. Edward Jones	33	face worker
77. Edwin Jones	34	haulier
78. James Jones	31	face worker
79. John Jones	20	face worker
80. John Jones	20	face worker
81. John Jones	41	face worker
82. John Giles Jones	64	repairer
83. Samuel Jones	43	haulier
84. William Jones	17	face worker
85. William John Jones	14	face worker
86. Thomas Lacey	19	haulier
87. Alfred Langley	15	face worker
88. Oliver Langley	41	haulier
89. Elias Lewis	13	face worker
90. James Lewis	31	haulier
91. John Lewis	17	haulier
92. Joseph Lewis	24	face worker
93. Lewis Lewis	25	face worker
94. Thomas Lewis	15	face worker
95. Thomas Lewis	36	face worker
96. Thomas Lewis	36	face worker
97. James Llewellyn	36	haulier
98. N. Loveridge	27	haulier
99. Frederick Martin	20	face worker
100. Edwin Mathews	42	face worker
101. Benjamin Meadows	53	face worker
102. James Meadows	31	face worker
103. William Morris	15	face worker
104. Henry Morgan	49	face worker
105. John Morgan	17	face worker
106. Thomas Morgan	24	face worker
107. Thomas Morgan	27	haulier
108. Thomas Morgan	41	repairer
109. Wm John Morgan	21	face worker
110. Thomas Oram	18	face worker
111. Frederick Parfitt	41	face worker
112. George Parfitt	13	face worker
113. Mark Parfitt	21	face worker
114. Ebenezer Phelps	22	face worker
115. Thomas Phillips	24	face worker
116. William Plenty	35	face worker
117. Albert Powell	14	face worker
118. Phillip Powell	29	face worker
119. Edmund Price	15	face worker
120. John Price	13	doorboy

121. James Pritchard	13	face worker
122. Joseph Pritchard	19	haulier
123. Rosser Pritchard	37	face worker
124. Thomas Pritchard	12	doorboy
125. William Reed	32	face worker
126. David Rees	25	haulier
127. David Rees	19	face worker
128. Joseph Rees	13	face worker
129. John Regan	16	face worker
130. William Regan	14	face worker
131. Edgar Robertson	14	face worker
132. Lewis Rogers	29	face worker
133. Watkin Rogers	36	glandman
134. William Rogers	13	knockerboy
135. George Rossiter	31	face worker
136. Thomas Ruck	21	face worker
137. George Rudge	27	haulier
138. John Samuel	22	face worker
139. Alfred Shaw	13	face worker
140. Charles Shaw	14	face worker
141. Sydney Shaw	37	haulier
142. Leonard Silcox	32	face worker
143. Richard Skye	28	repairer
144. Mathew Smith	29	face worker
145. Jeremiah Sullivan	14	face worker
146. Alfred Thomas	21	face worker
147. Charles Thomas	29	face worker
148. James Thomas	39	face worker
149. John Thomas	24	haulier
150. Joseph Thomas	29	haulier
151. William Thomas	18	face worker
152. Frank Trollope	40	face worker
153. George Trollope	29	face worker
154. James Tudgay	46	face worker
155. Joseph Tudgay	22	face worker
156. William Tudgay	32	hitcher
157. David Vater	61	face worker
158. Thomas Walbey	28	haulier
159. Albert Weaver	18	face worker
160. Daniel Webb	21	face worker
161. James Webb	22	face worker
162. John Webber	19	face worker
163. John White	28	repairer
164. Charles Wilcox	17	face worker
165. John Wilcox	54	face worker
166. Samuel Wilcox	21	face worker
167. John Williams	16	face worker
168. Thomas Williams	63	repairer

169. William Williams	34	bratticeman
170. William Williams	15	face worker
171. William Williams	64	face worker
172. William Williams	15	face worker
173. William Williams	35	face worker
174. William Williams	12	face worker
175. Wm Henry Williams	18	face worker
176. William Woods	16	face worker

Names of injured	*Occupation*
1. R. Ashman	fireman
2. Michael Birchael	labourer
3. George Bird	labourer
4. Ben Brain	labourer
5. Edward Currre	labourer
6. Edward Davies	doorboy
7. William Dee	doorboy
8. Edward Gullick	collier's boy
9. William Henry Gulliver	collier's boy
10. Aaron Higgs	doorboy
11. Edwin Higgs	collier's boy
12. Phillip Howard	collier's boy
13. Thomas Hughes	labourer
14. William Jenkins	
15. Arthur Jones	labourer
16. Cornelius Jones	labourer
17. William Jones	collier's boy
18. Edward Lockstone	labourer
19. Arthur Morgan	labourer
20. Mr Joseph Morgan	manager
21. Henry Oram	labourer
22. William Oram	labourer
23. Thomas Peggington	collier's boy
24. William Henry Peggington	collier's boy
25. Joseph Phelps	labourer
26. Thomas Phelps	labourer
27. Thomas Sulway	labourer

The inquest was held at Pontypool Town Hall and Thomas Williams, a local coal merchant, was the jury foreman. It was revealed that for the past thirty years the colliery had been worked by naked lights. Mr Edward Jones JP of Snatchwood, managing director of the company and the holder of an undermanager's certificate, said he thought it a perfectly safe practice. The verdict and opinion of the jury was accidental death. No one could be held to blame.

Llanerch Colliery was closed in September 1947 by the NCB.

The Llantrisant Colliery explosion at No.2 Shaft. At 1.45 p.m. on 2 June 1941 an explosion killed four men,. They were: John Gregor (agent/manager), Noab Fletcher (winding engineman), David Thomas (switch board attendant) and Ernest Evans (banksman). Most of the surface buildings and pithead was destroyed.

Llantrisant Colliery, Ynysmaerdy, Llantrisant, Glamorganshire

Llantrisant Colliery was opened in 1923. The explosion at Llantrisant Colliery in No.2 Pit on Whit Monday 2 June 1941 at 1.45 p.m. claimed the lives of John Gregor (agent/manager), Noab Fletcher (winding engineman), David Thomas (switch board attendant) and Ernest Evans (banksman).

Most of the surface buildings and pithead was destroyed. Llantrisant Colliery ceased production in 1941.

Lower Duffryn Colliery, Cwmpennar, Cynon Valley, Glamorganshire

Lower Duffryn Colliery was locally known as Cwmpennar, being in the village of Cwmpennar, and was opened in the 1851 by Thomas Powell. The colliery was owned by the Powell Duffryn Steam Coal Co. prior to nationalisation in 1947. An underground explosion on 25 February 1858 killed nineteen men and boys. Naked flame lights were in use. On 6 November 1860 a further twelve miners were killed by an explosion and naked flame lights were also in use.

The explosion at Lower Duffryn Colliery on Thursday 25 February 1858 claimed the lives of the following nineteen men and boys:

Names of casualties	Age	Occupation
1. William Aubrey snr	35	collier
2. William Aubrey jnr	12	collier's boy
3. George Cox	35	collier
4. Joseph Cox	15	doorboy
5. David Davies	19	collier
6. Levi Davies	45	collier
7. George Gale	15	doorboy
8. Daniel Jones	25	collier

Names of casualties	Age	Occupation
9. Owen Jones	18	haulier
10. Richard Jones	28	collier
11. John Morgan	24	collier
12. Henry Morris	18	haulier
13. Peter Norman	43	collier
14. Thomas Richards	15	collier's boy
15. John Rosser	32	collier
16. James Rumley	40	collier
17. Henry Salmon	11	collier's boy
18. Thomas Shawcross	32	collier
19. Edwin Strong	10	doorboy

On 1 January 1872 the accident reports show that forty-seven-year-old Benjamin Eynon was killed by falling down an air pit; on 20 March 1872 the accident reports show that twenty-one-year-old collier John Hopkins was killed underground by a fall of coal; on 10 July 1872 twelve-year-old labourer J.A. Jones was killed on the colliery surface by coal trucks; on 10 October 1872 the accident reports show that seventeen-year-old doorboy H. Prosser was killed underground when he was crushed by a horse; on 8 February 1873 the accident reports show that thirty-nine-year-old collier B. James was killed underground by a fall of coal and on 10 December 1886 the accident reports show that twenty-eight-year-old haulier David Price was killed underground by a journey of drams running wild 200 or 300 yards down an engine plane (main roadway), which overtook him and others, who were on their way to the pit bottom, the shackler having omitted to place his stop block across the rails below the landing, and when bringing the drams into place for the next journey having failed to scotch them. Lower Duffryn Colliery ceased coaling in 1927 and was kept open for pumping mine water until the colliery was demolished in the 1970s.

Llwynypia Colliery, Llwynypia, Rhondda Valley, Glamorganshire

Llwynypia Colliery height above Ordinance Datum 455ft, also known as the Glamorgan Colliery and the Scotch Colliery, was opened from 1861 by the Glamorgan Coal Co. and in 1910 it was part of the Cambrian concern with No.1 Pit employing 1,712 men, the No.2 Pit 1,539 and the No.5 Pit 656. At 7.30 p.m. on 25 January 1932 an explosion killed eleven miners, including two of the rescue team. A question of smoking was raised at the enquiry, but the cause of the explosion was never conclusively proved.

The explosion at Llwynypia Colliery on Monday 25 January 1932 claimed the lives of the following eleven men and boys:

Names of casualties	Names of casualties
1. J. Alsop	7. John Evans (rescuer)
2. Morgan Bowen	8. John Jones (rescuer)
3. Richard Cheney	9. David Rogers
4. Charles Crier	10. Clifford Sparrow
5. Stanley Dando	11. William Thomas
6. Henry Evans	

Llwynypia Colliery, Llwynypia, in 1918. It was situated at 455ft OD. Also known as the Glamorgan Colliery and the Scotch Colliery, it was opened in 1861 by the Glamorgan Coal Co. and in 1910 it was part of the Cambrian concern with No.1 Pit employing 1,712 men, the No.2 Pit, 1,539 and the No.5 Pit, 656. At 7.30 p.m. on 25 January 1932 an explosion killed eleven miners, including two of the rescue team. The colliery was owned by the Powell Duffryn Steam Coal Co., ceased producing coal in 1932 and was used for pumping mine water.

Llwynypia Colliery ceased producing coal in 1932 and was then used for pumping mine water.

Mardy No.1 and No.2 Colliery, Maerdy, Rhondda Valley, Glamorganshire

The Marquis of Bute declined the purchase of the 999-acre land and mineral rights of Maerdy Farm in 1847 and it was purchased in 1873 for £122,000, by Mordecai Jones. Additional capital was required for the hazardous task of sinking, and he then formed a partnership with Wheatley Cobb of Brecon. Mardy No.1 Pit was sunk in 1875 and Mardy No.2 Pit in 1976 to the Abergorki seam. The winding engine man was Daniel 'Eos Dar' Evans from Station Terrace, Maerdy when the explosion claimed eighty-one men and boys' lives on 23rd December 1885, his crossing 'Butty' was Morgan 'Engineer' Davies.

The morning of Wednesday 23 December 1885 saw 770 miners descend the Mardy No.1 and No.2 Pits, some, no doubt, with Christmas in their thoughts. At 2.45 p.m. there was a terrible explosion that heralded a bleak Christmas for many households at the village of Maerdy. There was an awful sadness that Christmas, the grief etched so vividly on memories that men and women 119 years later could still recall the terrible, numbing sense of loss that had been recalled to them by past members of their families.

They would tell how the sun rose on the morning of Wednesday 23 December 1885 over the mountains of the Rhondda Fach and shone on row after row of neat cottages, nearly all of them blighted by the tragedy, white blinds drawn over their windows. In some small front parlours, two or three bodies lay. Occasionally wails of anguish and a cry of 'O nhad annwyl' ('O, dear father') could be heard.

For Maerdy, the little village at the top of the valley, the nightmare which hovered over every mining community, the dreaded explosion in the Mardy Pit, had come horrifyingly true. Eighty-one men and boys had died in the blast at Mardy Pit on the day before Christmas Eve and cries of distress and hurryings to and fro echoed through the darkness of that night in 1885.

The village shook with the thunderous roar of the blast on the Wednesday afternoon. Pillars of smoke and dust poured from the shaft. So violent was the explosion that the cage was hurled to the headgear above its shaft. At the time 770 miners had been underground. Many escaped because they were working a coal seam 127 yards below. The majority of those who died succumbed to afterdamp, the chokedamp gas that comes after a firedamp explosion.

Roadman Levi Williams of 89 Maerdy Road, Maerdy, a miner of sixty, was among the dead. So was twelve-year-old collier boy William Jones of 11 Hill Street, Maerdy and thirteen-year-old collier boy Thomas Davies of 1 Thomas Street, Maerdy. Two more young boys might have perished but a collier risked his own life to rescue them when he heard their half suffocated cries of 'O, Mam, O, Mam' and 'Beth neiff mam nawr' ('What will mother do now'?). When the rescue team reached the underground air doors, lying face down was a young lad and when they moved his body they found his little dog, called 'Try'; the boy had tried to shield his little friend from the horrific event.

Thirty miners had been found uninjured but were so bewildered and paralysed by what had happened that they could not move. To reach them, rescuers passed many bodies as they made their way over smashed timber, rock falls and tangled wire ropes. The survivors had escaped death by staying where they were and not going where the afterdamp would have killed them.

Hundreds of men, women and children rushed to Mardy Pit. A mother seeing her son among the survivors brought to the surface screamed in delight and she fell upon his neck and burst into a passion of tears. About 9.00 a.m. the vast throng standing in the moonlight fell silent as word went around that large groups of rescued miners were coming up the pit. When the cage arrived at the surface it held four boys, not one aged more than fifteen-years of age. Tears flowed as relatives shouted their names, adding terms of affection in Welsh.

Fourteen-year-old doorboy Morgan Watkins of 6 Oxford Street, Maerdy, had escaped almost miraculously. His brother, seventeen-year-old haulier Thomas Watkins, also of 6 Oxford Street, Maerdy, had found him lying prostrate under the back legs of a pony pulling a dram.

By 10.30 p.m., all the rescued had been brought to the surface. Then came the dead. There was forty-nine-year-old Thomas Davies and his thirteen-year-old son, also Thomas Davies, of 1 Thomas Street, Maerdy, and another thirteen-year-old boy, John Edwards of 22 Thomas Street, Maerdy. And there was fifty-nine-year-old David Jones of 1 Pentre Road, Maerdy, a deacon of Seion Chapel, Maerdy Road, Maerdy. Survivor Morgan Davies of Maerdy Cottages, Maerdy, was to recall how he had been with him as they both struggled out of the workings after the explosion and after making a strenuous bid for freedom David Jones cried out, 'Oh Lord forgive me all my sins' and fell to the ground, dead.

They brought up from pit bottom 'Twm yr atgyfodiad' ('Resurrection Tom'). Resurrection Tom got his nickname while working at another colliery, where he wrote to his friends in West Wales and told them he was dead and buried. He then sat back and waited for his friends to turn up, which they duly did only to find Tom alive and kicking. Now Resurrection Tom was really dead.

At the cemetery, widows clung to relatives and found comfort in the soaring hymn singing, which seemed to lift the spirits of all present on the wings of eternal hope. Now, 120 years later, the poignancy of this Christmas tragedy, which orphaned seventy-two youngsters, still ripples out from the Rhondda Valley.

That Christmas one of the miners had been looking forward to spending time back home with his wife and children. He had no money to spare for trinkets for the children; instead he had bought four little loaves of bread to take home for a tea party. They found them in his lodgings when his body was taken back there from the pit. That Christmas took on the sombreness of Lent and sorrow silenced the carol singers.

As with most underground explosions, those who did not die as a result of the afterdamp had in many cases suffered severe burns or other horrific injuries. Some men, who had escaped the initial fury, were caught up in the aftermath of the explosion. One who had received only minor burns made his way to the stable area of the mine where, in total darkness, he slaked his thirst and bathed his wounds in a horse trough. Before he had finished, however, a mad pony rushed from the roadway, tumbled down the stable incline and fell dead, wedging the hapless miner against the trough. It was some considerable time before he could free himself and make his escape. Ultimately, the injuries he sustained from the collision with the horse were far worse than those from the blast.

On 1 January, the bodies of fifteen victims were removed from the houses where they had been laid. Decomposition was so advanced that distraught relatives wanted them to be taken to their own parishes to be buried without delay. The decision to remove the dead for burial without a Coroner's certificate was viewed by many as unlawful, but notes were issued by local doctors recommending immediate interment. Several corpses were so swollen that it was only with difficulty that the coffins could be closed and secured. The caskets were carried to the side of the railway to wait for a special train from Ferndale. The scene at the trackside was harrowing. The neat rows of coffins, each with its attendant group of grieving relatives, waited patiently in the early hours of the bitterly cold morning. After being put on board the trucks they began their journey to the many areas of South Wales from where the dead miners had come.

On the same day the Coroner arrived at the Commercial Hotel (the Anchor), Ferndale, and was greeted with a certain amount of hostility by the huge crowd that had gathered outside. He informed those waiting that he had only heard of the disaster on Wednesday evening and had at once contacted pit officials asking for full details. He had received no reply from either the manager or the owners, although both were duty bound to respond. It was, he added, only at the request of the police that he was present that day. The inquest was then formally adjourned until 12 January. That evening one of the survivors died from the injuries sustained in the aftermath of the blast.

The inquest resumed under the direction of Mr T. Williams and one of the first to take the stand was Griffith Thomas. He told the jury that the greatest force of the explosion had occurred in that part of the workings known as the Arches. This was an area of the mine where, for some 2,616 yards, naked lights were used to illuminate the roadway. When he was asked if such a state of affairs did not constitute a risk, he replied, 'The airway neutralised all harm'. He confirmed, however, that the mine was known to be both dusty and gaseous, yet despite this, shotfiring was allowed in all parts of the workings. After several days the court concluded, 'We find that an explosion of gas occurred in the Rhondda district of the Mardy Colliery on the 23rd December 1885. Where the gas ignited, sufficient evidence has not been produced for us to determine. We are however convinced that it did not occur from shotfiring in the hard heading'.

The jury appended the following suggestions:
1. That efficient means be taken to allay and then remove coal dust from mines generating explosive gases.

Right: Rescue and firefighting plans were kept at the colliery offices and ambulance room (medical centre). Before modernisation the medical centre was usually an old shed consisting of two rooms and totally inadequate to meet the demands of the workforce; it had poor lighting and sometimes no access for an ambulance.

Below: Large plain wound dressing. Dr S. Glanville Morris, chief surgeon for the Mardy Collieries, Maerdy, Rhondda Valley, Glamorganshire, was compiler of the first edition of the first-aid book. A large canister called a first-aid container was hung up in each district underground and contained a stretcher, splints, dressings and morphia injection containers.

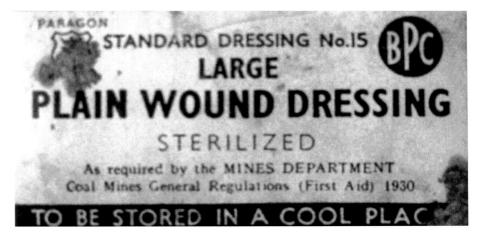

2. That boys attending elementary schools of the colliery district be taught the rules of the collieries in the vicinity of the schools.

One of the owners, William 'Bryn Awel' Thomas, was the first to descend the still-smoking shaft, leading the rescue operation and, in May 1886, he was awarded the Medal for Valour, for his 'coolness and devotion to humanity'.

The explosion at Mardy No.1 and No.2 Colliery on Wednesday 23 December 1885 at 2.45 p.m. claimed the lives of the following eighty-one men and boys:

Name	Age	Occupation	Residence, marital status
1. Joseph Baber	17	collier	61 Maerdy Road, Maerdy, single.
2. John Bevan	25	haulier	28 Hill Street, Maerdy, single.
3. Arthur Boozay	21	spragger	5 Oxford Street, Maerdy, single.
4. David Bowen	18	collier	21 Cemetery Road, Maerdy, single.
5. John Collins	40	collier	109 Maerdy Road, Maerdy, single.
6. Evan Davies	28	collier	6 Rowley Terrace, Maerdy, married with one child.
7. Evan Davies	19	collier	8 Hill Street, Maerdy, single.

Name	Age	Occupation	Residence, marital status
8. Isaac Davies	33	repairer	4 Wrgant Place, Maerdy, married with two children.
9. John Davies	17	collier boy	113 Maerdy Road, Maerdy, single.
10. Lewis Davies	32	mason	1 Maerdy Road, Maerdy, married with three children.
11. Thomas Davies	49	collier	1 Thomas Street, Maerdy, married with five children.
12. Thomas Davies	13	collier boy	1 Thomas Street, Maerdy, single.
13. William Davies	25	collier	35 Ferndale Road, Tylorstown, married with two children.
14. Edward Edwards	52	contractor	42 Oxford Street, Maerdy, married with nine children.
15. Edward Edwards	16	stoneman	42 Oxford Street, Maerdy, single.
16. John Edwards	13	collier boy	22 Thomas Street, Maerdy, single.
17. David Evans	16	collier boy	85 Maerdy Road, Maerdy, single.
✳18. John Evans	55	labourer	2 Rowley Terrace, Maerdy, married with three children.
19. John Evans	45	fireman	32 North Road, Ferndale, married with six children.
20. John Evans	25	collier	6 Rowley Terrace, Maerdy, single.
21. Richard Evans	24	collier	120 Maerdy Road, Maerdy, single.
22. Thomas Evans	26	collier	21 Pentre Road, Maerdy, married with three children.
23. Thomas Evans	26	haulier	17 Pentre Road, Maerdy, widower with one child.
24. Robert Griffiths	34	haulier	7 Hill Street, Maerdy, married with four children.
25. William Griffiths	16	collier	69 Oxford Street, Maerdy, single.
26. William Harries	29	collier	43 Maerdy Road, Maerdy, married with four children.
27. John Heard	22	collier	28 Pentre Road, Maerdy, single.
28. Ephraim Hughes	20	spragger	52 Maerdy Road, Maerdy, single.
29. Thomas Hughes	33	shackler	5 Ceridwen Street, Maerdy, married with two children.
30. Phillip Hutchins	35	hitcher	90 Maerdy Road, Maerdy, married with three children.
31. Henry Isaac	23	haulier	101 Maerdy Road, Maerdy, single.
32. Evan James	21	collier	18 Pentre Road, Maerdy, married.
33. Thomas Jenkins	25	cogman	52 Maerdy Road, Maerdy, single.
34. David Jones	20	miner	56 Maerdy Road, Maerdy, single.
35. David Jones	59	logman	1 Pentre Road, Maerdy, married with eight children.
36. David Jones	55	timberman	35 Pentre Road, Maerdy, married with one child.
37. David Jones	27	collier	5 Oxford Street, Maerdy, married.
38. David Jones	25	collier	23 Thomas Street, Maerdy, married with two children.
39. Isaac Jones	20	collier	12 Thomas Street, Maerdy, single.
40. John Jones	42	collier	11 Hill Street, Maerdy, married with four children.
41. John D. Jones	51	bratticeman	74 Maerdy Road, Maerdy, married with one child.
42. Joseph Jones	40	miner	82 Maerdy Road, Maerdy, single.
43. William Jones	12	collier boy	11 Hill Street, Maerdy, single.
44. William Jones	16	collier boy	21 Thomas Street, Maerdy, single.
45. David Lake	35	collier	40 Pentre Road, Maerdy, single.
46. David Lewis	40	collier	53 Maerdy Road, Maerdy, widower with four children.
47. John Lewis	19	collier	2 David Street, Ferndale, single.
48. Richard Lewis	46	collier	6 North Terrace, Maerdy, widower with one child.
49. James Loxton	28	labourer	13 Pentre Road, Maerdy, single.
50. Edmund Morgan	27	collier	52 Pentre Road, Maerdy, married.
51. Gomer Morgan	21	haulier	100 Maerdy Road, Maerdy, single.

Name	Age	Occupation	Residence, marital status
52. John Morgan	17	haulier	19 Hill Street, Maerdy, single.
53. James Parry	29	hitcher	107 Maerdy Road, Maerdy, married with one child.
54. Benjamin Phillips	40	roadman	2 Pit Row, Ferndale, married with six children.
55. David Phillips	50	mason	11 Thomas Street, Maerdy, married with five children.
56. Meshach Phillips	33	mason	75 Oxford Street, Maerdy, married.
57. Thomas Phillips	21	haulier	11 Thomas Street, Maerdy, single.
58. John Powell	23	hitcher	7 Rowley Terrace, Maerdy, single.
59. Owen Powell	28	collier	20 Llewellyn Street, Pontygwaith, married with three children.
60. Evan Pugh	17	collier	32 Oxford Street, Maerdy, single.
61. Henry Pullen	23	hitcher	25 Maerdy Road, Maerdy, single.
62. Phillip Richards	46	labourer	83 Maerdy Road, Maerdy, married with six children.
63. Evan Roberts	18	roadman	23 North Terrace, Maerdy, single.
64. David Rowlands	27	collier	19 Oxford Street, Maerdy, married with three children
65. Griffith Scourfield	19	labourer	86 Maerdy Road, Maerdy, single.
66. Joseph Spiller	22	collier	10 Maerdy Road, Maerdy, single.
67. Michael Stokes	17	haulier	1 Maerdy Huts, Maerdy, single.
68. James Sutton	28	labourer	13 Pentre Road, Maerdy, single.
69. David Thomas	19	collier	4 Maerdy Huts, Maerdy, single.
70. Edward Thomas	23	rider	24 Pentre Road, Maerdy, married with one child.
71. James Thomas	24	collier	108 Maerdy Road, Maerdy, married.
72. John Henry Thomas	23	miner	9 Thomas Street, Maerdy, single.
73. Thomas Thomas	24	miner	29 Pentre Road, Maerdy, single.
74. William Thomas	19	collier	33 Pentre Road, Maerdy, single.
75. Owen Tudor	32	miner	2 Rowley Terrace, Maerdy, married with three children.
76. Morgan Watkins	14	doorboy	6 Oxford Street, Maerdy, single.
77. Thomas Watkins	17	haulier	6 Oxford Street, Maerdy, single.
78. Daniel Williams	43	overman	33 North Road, Ferndale, married with seven children.
79. John Williams	25	collier	52 Pentre Road, Maerdy, single.
80. Levi Williams	60	roadman	89 Maerdy Road, Maerdy, married with three children.
81. William Williams	30	miner	13 North Terrace, Maerdy, married.

Names of injured

1. Richard Davies, 28 Ceridwen Street, Maerdy, had burns on his head, face, hands and body and was a bad case.
2. John Jones, 90 Mardy Road, Maerdy, had burns on his head, face and hands and was a favourable case.
3. Mr. Lewis, 127 Mardy Road, Maerdy, had slight burns on his hands and face and was a favourable case.
4. Gomer Rees, The Huts, Maerdy, had burns on his head, face, hands and body and was a very bad case.
5. John Williams, 24 Oxford Street, Maerdy, had burns on his head, face, hands and body and was a very serious case.

Mardy No.1 and No.2 Colliery Rescue team in the 1930s. The rescue team was supplied with the very latest life-saving equipment and were fully trained for any emergency including underground fires and explosions. Today the Dinas Mines Rescue Station continues to serve South Wales, the Forest of Dean and the West Country Mines.

Mardy No.1 and No.2 Colliery rescue team in the 1930s. When the rescue team reached the underground air doors, lying face down was a young lad and when they moved his body they found his little dog, called 'Try', his faithful friend and loving companion. The boy had tried to shield his little friend from the horrific event of the explosion.

There were thirty-eight pit ponies underground at the time of the explosion, but only fifteen survived. Jack and Jerry, two Welsh ponies, were not found until Boxing Day and when brought together made a terrible fuss of each other. Finally being brought to the surface and led to green pastures.

Mining disasters have woven a dark pattern of tragedy throughout the history of coal mining. These catastrophes live on in the memories of the people to be recalled from time to time. One of the best remembered in the Rhondda Valley, perhaps because it happened within two days of Christmas Day, is the explosion at Mardy No.1 and No.2 Colliery on Wednesday 23 December 1855.

On Saturday 9 April 1949 there were eight disaster survivors still living in the village of Maerdy and they recalled the 1885 explosion. What is amazing is that in April 1949 there were a dozen living survivors of the disaster and, out of that number, eight resided in Maerdy. The oldest at that time was Mr Robert Jones, an eighty-five-year-old formerly of 12 Richard Street, Maerdy, and who was confined to his bed. Mr Jones was twenty-one at the time of the explosion. He was in charge of a horse which he rescued by throwing a bag over its head. It was the only horse in the district to come out of the pit alive. Three days after the disaster Mr Jones was married but what should have been a joyous occasion was marred by his grim duty of helping to carry some of the bodies of the pit victims over the Aberdare Mountain. On the other side of Richard Street at No.67 lived seventy-nine-year-old Mr Thomas Thomas, a native of Abercrave, Swansea. He went to work in Mardy No.1 and No.2 Colliery with his father when he was only twelve years old. He remembered that shortly before the explosion officials had been around selling tickets for the Christmas concert to be held in Maerdy. Mr Thomas Thomas was working in the far end and luckily came out safely. His namesake, seventy-seven-year-old Mr Thomas Thomas, formerly of 1 Brook Terrace, Maerdy, and a composer and choir leader, said he will never forget the experience.

Seventy-seven-year-old Mr William Henry Lewis formerly of 16 Blake Street, Maerdy, was a doorboy working in the little south district on that fateful day. He had left the haulier with whom he was working to order drams for the next journey. The haulier was killed and Mr Henry Lewis was found unconscious not far from the pit bottom by Mr Griffith Thomas the colliery manager.

Mr Thomas Davies formerly of 12 Griffiths Street, Maerdy, was working with his father in the far end when he was twelve years old. Mr Thomas Davies knew that something was wrong and a door of brattice was placed across the roadway to prevent anyone from going through. The men and boys had to wait until 6.00 p.m. to be brought up the pit through No.1 shaft. The explosion was in No.2 shaft. His brother, seventy-six-year-old Mr Samuel Davies, formerly of 79 Richard Street, claimed to be the youngest survivor. He was working as a doorboy with Thomas Thomas, formerly of 67 Richard Street, Maerdy, and had been employed in Mardy Pit for only four-and-a-half-months when the explosion took place. He was at the far end. Thankfully nobody had been injured in that district.

Eighty-four-year-old Mr David 'Cymro' Jones, formerly of 78 James Street, Maerdy, told a graphic story. Mr David 'Cymro' Jones had a remarkably active personality. At the time of the disaster, he was one of four lodging with Mrs Pritchard, formerly of Maerdy Road, Maerdy. For days they had noticed a peculiar smell in the house and on the morning of the tragedy a flash went through the room, causing the landlady to exclaim, 'Did you see that flash boys?' All had seen the flash except one. That one lost his life and his body was taken home enshrouded in brattice cloth. This cloth gave out the strange odour that had been in the air of the house for several days. Mr David 'Cymro' Jones was working on the Aberdare side of the pit and for some time was unaware that there had been an explosion. He actually filled a half dram of coal after it happened. He came up the pit, but went down again two hours later to assist with his brother in searching for the bodies.

Mardy No.1 and No.2 Colliery ambulance brigade in the 1920s. Mardy No.1 squad became famous for being the holders of the Sir C. Warren Rhondda Shield, the Glamorgan County Shield and the Provincial White Horse Shield, besides being the holder of three champion cups and eight gold and silver medals.

Mardy No.1 and No.2 Colliery Maerdy in the 1880s. Mardy Colliery No.1 Pit stood at 949ft OD, National Grid ref. 97369885.

Eighty-two-year-old Mr William Evans, formerly of 22 Royal Cottages, Maerdy, came to Maerdy from Fishguard when he was fourteen years old. Mr William Evans was working in No.2 north deep when the explosion happened. The lamps were blown out and he was hurled several yards but he had not realised what had taken place. His butty Jimmy Thomas was killed but he escaped uninjured. In 1915, however, he was badly injured in the pit and had undergone nine operations on his leg. He had to walk with the aid of crutches and, owing to the liquidation of the company, he did not receive any compensation. These veterans presented a strangely moving picture when they shook hands outside Maerdy Workmen's Hall in April 1949. They had looked death in the face when they were only boys. They had met once again with dignity about their silvered heads and an obvious pride in looking their best.

At twelve noon on 25 August 1893 the accident reports show that forty-year-old tipper Richard Hughes was seriously injured when he was crushed between some drams while tipping at the screens on the colliery surface. He died on 2 September 1893; on 19 January 1896 the accident reports show that twenty-two-year-old oil girl (who oiled and greased machinery on the colliery surface) Louisa Thomas was killed on the colliery surface by a dram running wild down the surface incline and on 13 November 1894 the accident reports show that fifty-nine-year-old assistant roadman Thomas Williams was killed underground by a fall of roof in the Four-Feet coal seam. Mardy No.1 and No.2 Colliery was closed in 1940.

Mardy No.3 and No.4 Colliery, Maerdy, Rhondda Valley, Glamorganshire

Mardy No.3 Pit was opened in 1893 and No.4 Pit was opened in 1914 by Lockets-Merthyr Steam Coal Co. On 1 January 1947, with the coming of nationalisation, Mardy Colliery was placed in the National Coal Board's South Western Division, No.4 (Aberdare) Area and at that time employed five men underground and ten men on the surface on a maintenance basis.

The following is an interview with miner Howard 'Chippo' Jones on Thursday 8 June 2000:

On Friday 19th March 1965 my butty Harry Millard and myself was working on a development road called the F14 and we were told by a colliery official to stop working on the road and go into the F13 coal-face because there were men missing on the 2:15 p.m. afternoon shift and we had to cover the missing men and put two packs up.

We then heard the afternoon shift was in dispute because we had been put to work in the F13 coal-face. There was no one missing in fact they had a full team. It was 3:45 p.m. when the men arrived at the face and by this time my butty Harry and myself had completed one pack and was half way in completing the second pack when suddenly there was an explosion. I was knocked over by the blast and the next thing I realized was my hair and the clothes on my back was on fire. I put the flames out by stripping to the waist and I had some bad burns".

"We all made our way to the waiting spake and when I arrived in hospital a nurse asked me if there was any one else coming in with burns. I said, 'No all the rest was to green to burn'. "I spent two weeks in hospital.

The explosion was caused by shotfiring and fortunately there were no fatalities. Following their convalescence salt of the earth Howard 'Chippo' Jones and butty Harry Millard worked on the surface at Mardy Colliery until their retirement.

Date	Names of injured	Registration No.	Occupation and nature of accident
29 October 1968	Syd Tibbles	2246	Assistant electrician. Wrenched left shoulder muscles. Attended by Sister Enfys Hughes.
23 May 1969	Bob Challenger	1083	Overman. Cut on left cheek. Attended by Cullen Morris. Reg No.2059.
25 June 1969	Dennis Morris	2397	Repairer. Abrasions and bruises on left hand. Attended by Sister Enfys Hughes.
1 December 1970	Will Sly	0225	Collier. Cut his scalp. Attended by Sister Enfys Hughes.
8 January 1971	Byron Seldon	2439	Winding engineman. Bruised right arm and elbow. Attended by George Leach.
7 October 1972	Ken Chick	0533	Dismantler. Bruised third finger on left hand. Attended by George Leach.
11 October 1972	R. Ayres	1595	Collier. Burns on hand and arm. Attended by Dai Philpott. Reg. No.0440.
3 November 1972	S. Jones	2475	Repairer. Cut right eyelid. Attended by Tony Mason. Reg. No.2894.
21 December 1972	B.N. Jones	0310	Collier. Bruised right arm. Attended by George Leach. Reg. No.0404.

Date	Names of injured	Registration No.	Occupation and nature of accident
30 January 1973	Glyn Edwards	0889	Pipeman. Strained muscle in lower back. Attended by George Leach.
26 March 1973	G. Lloyd	2472	Repairer. Bruised knuckles on right hand. Attended by Sister Enfys Hughes.
20 April 1973	Mike Morgan	1059	Borer. Bruises and abrasions to the nose. Attended by George Leach.
6 June 1973	Billy England	0010	Collier. Cut left cheek. Attended by George Leach.
13 April 1974	George Francis	0130	Official. Bruised right wrist. Attended by Ross Jones. Reg. No.2343.
21 July 1974	Em J. Crutch	2425	Fitter. Lacerations to third finger on the right hand. Attended by George Leach.
7 February 1975	John 'Hank' Hanley	1287	Repairer. Bruised left side of chest. This man refused to go for an X Ray. Attended by George Leach.
1 March 1975	D.G. Jones	2485	Collier. Bruised corner of right eye. Attended by Ross Jones.
13 March 1975	P. Rees	0416	Collier. Strained his left arm. Attended by Cullen Morris.
8 April 1975	Mike Rees	1852	Collier. Laceration under left eyebrow. He would not go to hospital, advised to see GP. Attended by George Leach.

Excerpt from Mardy No.3 and No.4 Colliery Special Bulletin Newsletter, Friday 29 April 1977:

On Monday 25th April 1977 at approximately 10:05 a.m. a tragic accident occurred, seriously injuring 3 workmen and injuring 3 others. A runaway pair of tubs (one ton drams) went out of control down a 1 in 4 drift, striking some of the injured and trapping two others. Within 1½ hours the injured were freed, treated for first aid and whisked away by ambulance from the colliery to East Glamorgan Hospital. Two doctors rushed to the colliery, namely Dr Davies, who went down to pit bottom, and Dr Daly, who attended on the surface, and could only commend the speedy and efficient way in which the injured were brought to the surface.

Dr Evans, NCB Area Medical Officer and Mr Caldwell, Area First Aid Superintendent, who attended the injured in the medical centre, gave the highest praise for the first aid administered to the injured: "I specifically wish to express my admiration and appreciation to all those persons who were involved in the initial freeing, treatment and conveying of the injured from the accident scene, being well aware that all concerned went far beyond the normal call of duty and their usual jobs. There is no doubt at all that had it not been for the prompt and selfless work of all those people involved the effect upon those injured, although serious enough, would have been far more grave. I thank also the people who cared medically for them – our own NCB Medical Staff, the Doctors (both NCB and local), the Ambulance Men and the Nursing and Medical Staff of East Glamorgan Hospital. The colliery personnel who notified relatives and, where required, ferried them to the hospital. The organisations, both in and outside of the pit, the NUM, NACODS and NCB management, also HM Inspectors, who spent many hours at the pit investigating the accident. The Police who readily and spontaneously proffered every assistance. The Mayor of Rhondda, who was concerned enough to personally visit the Colliery. The witnesses interviewed, who gave their evidence concisely, honestly and without fear of any possible reprisals. Again to the men at the scene, thank you, a sentiment which I feel sure the injured and their relatives would also like me to express on their behalf. I would like to conclude by saying that we all sincerely hope that the injured will make a good recovery".

K. Pearce (acting manager).

The accident at Mardy Colliery on Monday 25 April 1977 at approximately 10.05 a.m. injured the following five men and one boy:

Names of seriously injured	Occupation
1. Albert 'Snowy' Cavell	fireman
2. Glyn James	fitter
3. Dennis Piper	overman
4. Jimmy Hayes	supplyman
5. Mervyn 'Merky' Jones	supplyman
6. Gwyn 'Sheep' Rossiter	trainee

Large reserves of coal were still to be worked at Mardy Colliery for an estimated 100 years. Mardy No.3 and No.4 Colliery, the last deep coal mine in the Rhondda Valley, was closed on Thursday 21 December 1990 by British Coal.

McLaren Colliery, Abertysswg, Rhymney Valley, Glamorganshire

When great darkness covered the valley, a roaring boom shook the whole community. McLaren No.1 Colliery commenced sinking in August 1897 by the Tredegar Iron Co. By July 1898 it was linked to Bedwellty Pits and in 1899 it was linked to McLaren No.2 Pit, then called Pwll Laca. The colliery was named after Sir Charles McLaren. The third shaft commenced sinking in January 1906 and was completed to a depth of 1,098ft in June 1907.

On Wednesday 3 September 1902 at 11.30 p.m. great darkness covered the valley after an explosion of firedamp in the Yard Vein coal seam, which was caused by working near to or in a large accumulation of gas, killing sixteen miners, the youngest being seventeen years of age and the eldest forty-one, and injured twenty-one others. Two pit ponies also lost their lives. Approximately 120 miners were working at the time of the explosion, using safety flame lamps.

The explosion at McLaren Colliery on 3 September 1902 claimed the lives of the following sixteen men and boys:

Names of casualties	Age	Occupation	Residence
1. William Baker	24	timberman	Prospect Place, Tredegar
2. William H. Brawn	32	timberman	54 Queen Street, Tredegar
3. Evan H. Evans	25	timberman	6 McLaren Cottages, Abertysswg
4. George Grainger	32	haulier	86 Lower Road, Cwmsifiog
5. Walter Griffiths	25	collier	40 Charles Street, Tredegar
6. John Jones	30	timberman	The Garn, Tredegar
7. J.T. Jones	23	collier	14 Arthur Street, Abertysswg
8. Rees Jones	26	haulier	26 High Street, Tredegar
9. W.J. Jones	17	haulier	30 East Street, Tredegar

Names of casualties	Age	Occupation	Residence
10. Thomas Minton	37	collier	Rhymney Valley
11. Gwilym Morgan	41	collier	7 Charles Street, Tredegar
12. Azariah Probert	25	collier	7 Cross Street, Rhymney
13. William Rawlings	25	labourer	22 Fothergill Street, New Tredegar
14. Gwilym Roberts	34	collier	103 Vale Terrace, Tredegar
15. George Wilkins	41	haulier	10 Charles Street, Tredegar
16. Albert Williams	19	haulier	10 Upper Stanley Street, New Tredegar

On 12 April 1900 the accident reports show that forty-eight-year-old haulier Thomas Jones was killed when he was stepping into the pit cage at a mouthing in the shaft. He fell a distance of forty yards to the bottom in consequence of the hitcher signalling the cage away while he was standing on the platform between the cage and the landing; on 27 October 1902 the accident reports show that twenty-nine-year-old journey rider James Davies was killed underground when he was riding between the third and fourth drams of a journey of nine going up the main roadway slope. The front wheel of the first dram broke when going over the crossing at No.2 parting and thus threw the rest of the journey off the rails. He was dragged about ten yards; on 3 November 1902 the sixty-year-old surface foreman William Taylor was killed on the colliery surface while assisting a new hand to work a tippler (a tippler is a mechanical device used to tip drams of coal on to the screens of a colliery) at the screens (the screens are on the colliery surface where coal was sorted into different sizes and any rubbish in the coal was picked out in preparation for its final destination to domestic or industry customers); he was crushed by a full dram which he had not noticed coming from the weigh machine; on 1 June 1903 the accident reports show that sixty-year-old labourer Rees Perrott was fatally injured; on 11 March 1904 the accident reports show that forty-four-year-old fireman Thomas Lodwick was killed underground when he was walling in front of a row of insufficiently spragged coal and the coal fell upon him. On 27 October 1904 twenty-two-year-old collier Edward Williams was fatally injured. McLaren Colliery was merged with Ogilvie Colliery in July 1958 and was closed in 1969 by the NCB.

Morfa Colliery, Margam Moors, Near Port Talbot, Glamorganshire

Morfa Colliery (Abbot Pit and Grange Pit) was sunk in 1847 to supply coal to the Taibach Copper Works. The colliery was owned by C.R.M. Talbot Esquire and leased to Messrs Vivian and Sons. Morfa had an unfortunate history of seven explosions (June 1849, May 1850, December 1850, November 1858, October 1863, February 1870, March 1890) and it became known as the Pit of Ghosts.

In June 1849 an explosion killed collier Richard Williams and badly burned three other miners; in May 1850 an explosion badly burnt six miners, on Wednesday 11 December 1850 an explosion killed three miners instantly and thirteen more miners eventually died from their injuries.

At approximately 1.00 a.m. on 26 November 1858 an explosion killed four miners. The bodies and the evidence of the explosion were only discovered in the normal routine course of the night overman's inspection of the districts.

The top of Aaron Charlton's safety lamp had been removed and found in his pocket was a self-made key that fitted the lamp's lock.

The explosion at Morfa Colliery on 26 November 1858 claimed the following four miners' lives:

Names of casualties	Age	Occupation
1. Aaron Charlton	38	collier
2. Isaac Griffiths	25	collier
3. David Hughes	35	collier
4. William Williams	24	collier

On 23 August 1860 the accident reports show that thirty-three-year-old collier J. Hewitt was killed under the cage whilst it was in motion; on 3 September 1860 the accident reports show that fifty-five-year-old shoer T. Jenkins was killed when he was attempting to get into the cage whilst it was in motion; on 17 September 1860 forty-year-old collier T. Charles was killed when he was leaving the cage whilst it was in motion, and on 6 July 1860 sixteen-year-old signal boy William Rosser was killed underground when he was run over by a journey of drams.

At approximately 10.00 a.m. on 17 October 1863 another explosion killed thirty-nine miners. On this fateful day, night overmen John Evans and William Dommer reported the district to be free of gas and 400 men went down to work the dayshift. Mr William Grey the manager followed them at about 9.30 a.m. and undermanager Mr William Barrass at 10.00 a.m. The cage carrying the undermanager gave an ominous shudder and he guessed the worst. The blast shattered the west side of the old Nine-Feet district, where there were said to be numerous abandoned workings in which gas, quite commonly, accumulated. Mr William Grey became a very ill man as the consequence of his exertions fighting his way through falls. Despite their reputation naked flame lights were still in use as late as 1870.

The explosion at Morfa Colliery on Saturday 17 October 1863 claimed the lives of the following thirty-nine men and boys:

Names of casualties	Names of casualties
1. John Arford	21. Herbert Griffiths
2. John Bevan	22. David Morgan
3. Thomas Coxer	23. Evan Morgan
4. Michael Croly	24. Thomas Morris
5. John Daniel	25. Thomas Morris
6. John David	26. William Nicholas
7. Samuel Davies	27. William Prosser
8. John Edwards	28. Hopburn Richards
9. David Grey	29. Thomas Richards
10. William Grey	30. William Roberts
11. William Hopkins	31. John Stevens
12. Thomas Hunt	32. Peter Sutton
13. Benjamin James	33. John Tanner
14. Humphrey Jenkins	34. John Thomas
15. Joseph Johner	35. Thomas Thomas
16. William Jones	36. Thomas Thomas
17. William Jones	37. Henry Wilkins
18. William Lewis	38. Nathaniel Williams
19. Thomas Lodwick	39. Rees Williams
20. David Mathew	

On 14 February 1870 another explosion killed thirty miners. The shafts at the colliery were being deepened to the lower seams. A keg holding approximately 40lbs of blasting powder was kept in an engine-house near pit bottom. It was ignited here, so management asserted that it was responsible for the deaths on this day of thirty miners. Others said that the effects of such a blast could not have been felt at the stables about 600 yards distance inbye ('he has gone inbye' means he has gone towards the coalface). They were proved to be very inaccurate. All of the thirty-two horses kept in the stables were found dead.

About ten days after the explosion, men at work clearing the falls and erecting new timber supports were using naked flame lights; one of them, a lad named James Badge, was observed walking to join a gang, with a naked torch in his hands. There came an ignition of gas at his torch 'and the hand holding the flaming flambeau was almost entirely burnt away'. The manager at this time was Mr William Gay. At the inquest he said that on 6 February a patch of coal in the Nine-Feet coal seam had taken fire and the shift overman on duty thought it was not worth reporting. He was dismissed for neglecting his duties.

The explosion (locally known as the Cornish explosion) at Morfa Colliery on Monday 14 February 1870 claimed the lives of the following thirty men and boys:

Names of casualties
1. William Bennet
2. Thomas Blatworth
3. James Brian
4. William Cardon
5. Benjamin Coade
6. Jeremiah Crocker
7. William Crowning
8. James Davies
9. John Davies
10. William Dummer
11. Henry Francis
12. Thomas Francis
13. Michael Grace
14. John Hall
15. William Harris

Names of casualties
16. Daniel Hickey
17. John Horley
18. Henry Jones
19. Andrew Manning
20. John Manning
21. Robert Peel
22. William Row
23. Thomas Spargoe
24. Thomas Thomas
25. John Vanstone
26. Thomas Vanstone
27. John Waters
28. John Williams
29. Llewellyn Williams
30. Thomas Williams

On 10 August 1874 the accident reports show that stoker M. Dixon was killed by an internal flue of a boiler when it collapsed on him; on 26 February 1884 the accident reports show that forty-year-old collier Samuel Smokeam was killed underground when he fell under a journey of drams and on 27 August 1889 the accident reports show that fourteen-year-old messenger William Flemming was killed on the colliery surface when he fell in front of a locomotive and was run over.

On 10 March 1890 another explosion killed eighty-seven miners. At this time Morfa Colliery was producing 400 tons of coal a day from the Nine-Feet and the Cribber coal seams and on a Tuesday morning a little after midnight there came a violent explosion in the latter of these districts that was to take eighty-seven men and boys' lives. Safety flame oil lamps were in use.

Two rescue parties went down the pit and got themselves into serious difficulties caused by the afterdamp. Afterdamp is the atmosphere produced by an explosion of gas in a mine, consisting of carbonic acid, nitrogen and steam. The deadly mixture of gases following an explosion in a colliery is mainly composed of carbon monoxide and could kill more miners than the explosion itself. There were approximately 250 miners underground at the time of the explosion.

The explosion at Morfa Colliery on Tuesday 10 March 1890 claimed the lives of the following eighty-seven men and boys:

Names of casualties	Age	Occupation
1. Mr William Barras	48	manager
2. Griffith Bevan	32	collier
3. Daniel Brownsill	40	explorer
4. Daniel Buckley	29	pumpsman
5. John Buckley	35	pumpsman
6. Wm H. Clatworthy	18	pumpsman
7. William Cornick	50	packer
8. Thomas Daniel	14	doorboy
9. James David	40	collier
10. Thomas David	47	repairer
11. David Davies	33	repairer
12. Ebenezer Davies	36	collier
13. Meredith Davies	39	collier
14. Thomas Davies	19	hitcher
15. Evan Eley	37	collier
16. Edward Ellis	51	collier
17. Edward Floyd	32	collier
18. William Francis	28	collier
19. Daniel Griffiths	42	collier
20. John Griffiths	42	collier
21. Samuel Griffiths	50	collier
22. Bethuel Haycock	19	haulier
23. Evan Hedley	40	repairer
24. Joseph Hicks	20	repairer
25. David Hopkins	48	haulier
26. T. Hopkins	52	collier
27. John Hopton	38	haulier
28. Samuel Howell	46	collier
29. William James snr	40	collier
30. William James jnr	16	collier
31. Frederick Jenkins	16	greaser
32. Daniel John	57	collier
33. David Jones	52	collier
34. John Jones	37	collier
35. Joseph Jones	40	collier
36. William Jones	32	collier
37. William Jones	18	hitcher
38. Thomas Kemp	19	haulier
39. Patrick Kennedy	46	pumpsman
40. David King	38	collier
41. Benjamin Lewis	29	collier
42. John Lewis	38	collier
43. Simeon Lewis	40	collier
44. Thomas Lewis	40	collier

Names of casualties	Age	Occupation
45. William Lewis	46	collier
46. William Lewis	34	collier
47. John Leyshon	35	repairer
48. Thomas Leyshon	48	collier
49. Thomas Leyshon	30	collier
50. William Leyshon	50	collier
51. Richard Lucas	36	haulier
52. Noah Mandry	50	collier
53. Thomas Mandry	27	collier
54. David Mathews	30	collier
55. T. Miles	48	collier
56. Evan Morgan	20	signalman
57. Evan Morgan	21	collier
58. John Morris	46	collier
59. John Morris	46	overman
60. John Nicholas	28	collier
61. John Nichols	62	doorboy
62. Thomas Oates jnr	20	collier
63. Henry Parker	30	labourer
64. Alfred Phillips	40	collier
65. John Pippin	39	collier
66. D. Price	36	collier
67. John Ready	50	repairer
68. David Rees	40	ostler
69. Lewis Rees	42	collier
70. David Richards	36	collier
71. William Scott	29	collier
72. William Taylor jnr	15	haulier
73. Evan Thomas	34	collier
74. Joseph Thomas	50	collier
75. William Thomas	32	collier
76. James Tippott	17	haulier
77. William Vanstone	32	collier
78. Isaac Walters	23	fanman
79. Richard Walters	49	collier
80. David Williams	46	collier
81. David Williams	19	hitcher
82. Henny Williams	70	repairer
83. Isaac Williams	50	collier
84. James Williams	16	haulier
85. Tom Henry Williams	32	repairer
86. David Wilde	40	roadman
87. Thomas Yorwerth	38	haulier

At 7.20 p.m. on 5 June 1895 the accident reports show that twenty-seven-year-old rider David Jones was killed underground when he was crushed by a journey of empty drams on an engine

plane, the hook at the end of a draw-bar broke and threw him off while he was riding up in front of the four drams; on 14 July 1897 the accident reports show that nineteen-year-old haulier George Collins was killed underground when he was crushed against a collar (a collar is a wooden roof support, consisting of two arms [wooden posts] and a collar. When erected the collar would be firmly tightened against the roof with wooden wedges) while riding on the shaft of a journey, the roadway was 4ft 5ins in height; at 1.15 p.m. on 9 March 1900 twenty-seven-year-old collier W. Howell was seriously injured underground on a road in the Cribbwr coal seam by a clift 6ft 6ins x 2ft x 2ft in thickness, the clift fell between two pairs of timbers while he was sitting down waiting for his lamp to be returned to him by the haulier to whom he had lent it. He died the next day on 10 March 1900. On 25 October 1909 the accident reports show that forty-year-old collier John Payne was the last miner fatally injured underground up to the abandonment of Morfa Colliery in 1914.

Naval Colliery, Penygraig, Rhondda Valley, Glamorganshire

Naval Colliery, Penygraig, was locally known as the Pandy Pit and was opened in 1875 by Moses Rowlands Junior, the chief partner in a company known as the Naval Colliery Co. The Anthony Pit was opened in 1910. In 1913 the colliery employed 850 and in 1947 employed 808 miners. On 13 February 1872 the accident reports show that forty-eight-year-old collier W. Samuel was killed underground by a fall of roof; on 28 November 1873 the accident reports also show that twenty-three-year-old collier John Jones was killed underground by a fall of roof and on 4 December 1875 the accident reports also show that colliers T. Jones and Z. Williams were drowned underground by an influx of water from old workings. The colliery was owned by the Powell Duffryn Steam Coal Co. prior to nationalisation in 1947. On 10 December 1880 there was an explosion at the Naval Colliery which claimed the lives of 101 men and boys. On 27 January 1884 another explosion claimed the lives of eleven miners and a further three belonging to the rescue team were suffocated while exploring after the explosion.

Overman David Lewis reported the mine clear of all gas and at 7.00 p.m. descended the pit with the night shift. The high pressure of air that came from the explosion on 10 December 1880 burst out at the top of the upcast shaft. Falls were very heavy and extensive but several survivors were rescued, the youngest being fourteen-year-old Samuel Lewis and the eldest casualty seventy-year-old David Lloyd of Trealaw, which was just a short stroll away from the pit. The inquest decided that the initial sheet of flame had been fuelled by the large quantity of coal dust in the atmosphere and this had not only raised the temperature of the inferno but had carried it into areas that were free of gas.

The explosion at Naval Colliery on Friday 10 December 1880 claimed the lives of the following 101 men and boys:

Names of casualties	Age	Names of casualties	Age
1. Henry Brooks	28	7. W.R. David	23
2. James Chadwick	25	8. Evan Davies	32
3. Archibald Cooke	27	9. Evan Davies	15
4. Charles David	24	10. John Davies	42
5. Evan David	49	11. John Davies	25
6 .William T. David	21	12. John Davies	25

Names of casualties	Age	Names of casualties	Age
13. William Davies	26	58. Edward Job Morgan	66
14. W. Roderick Davies	23	59. James Morgan	75
15. Thomas Edwards	59	60. John Morgan	33
16. David Evans	26	61. Joseph Morgan	25
17. David Evans	23	62. Morgan Morgan	28
18. Howell Evans	45	63. Thomas Morgan	17
19. John Evans	35	64. William Morgan	56
20. William Evans	38	65. Joseph Morris	32
21. James Francis	50	66. Thomas Morris	36
22. Alfred Fry	30	67. James Murphy	50
23. William Fry	27	68. William Parlour	29
24. Griffith George	24	69. William Pearce	37
25. James Gibbon	20	70. Evan Phillips	19
26. Zephaniah Gibbon	36	71. Eli Rapps	29
27. Thomas Grice	21	72. Evan Radcliffe	30
28. William Grice	23	73. Thomas Reed	29
29. Evan Griffiths	22	74. Evan Rees	27
30. William Howell	21	75. John Rees	34
31. Benjamin Howells	52	76. David Roberts	31
32. Edward Hughes	42	77. William Roblin	40
33. John Hughes	29	78. Noah Rogers	39
34. Henry Isaacs	32	79. David Rosser	20
35. Thomas Isaac	28	80. George Samuel	30
36. James Jenkins	40	81. Phillip Samuel	18
37. John Jenkins	42	82. Samuel Samuel	14
38. Rees John	19	83. Thomas Simon	23
39. Evan Jones	45	84. John Snook	52
40. Henry Jones	32	85. John Stone	48
41. Joseph Jones	30	86. David Thomas	33
42. Thomas Jones	36	87. John Thomas	18
43. Thomas Jones	31	88. Morgan Thomas	25
44. Thomas Jones	21	89. Thomas Thomas	31
45. Thomas H. Jones	25	90. David Watkins	44
46. David Lewis	43	91. Sydney Welding	15
47. Edward Lewis	42	92. David Williams	59
48. James Lewis	15	93. David D. Williams	36
49. Richard Lewis	24	94. Evan Williams	35
50. Samuel Lewis	14	95. Griffith Williams	22
51. William Lewis	56	96. James Williams	38
52. William Lewis	49	97. John R. Williams	23
53. David Lloyd	70	98. Richard Williams	49
54. John Lloyd	40	99. Robert Williams	16
55. David Lodowick	45	100. Thomas Williams	40
56. William Marksman	26	101. Thomas Williams	32
57. John Willis McCarthy	32		

Early on Sunday morning 27 January 1884 the officials descended the pit in preparation for the coaling shift on Monday morning. They fired a round of shots off in the coal and it is thought that one of the shots was the cause of the explosion. The blast was so powerful it drove the cage up into the headgear and demolished the fan house and damaged the fan itself. Thomas Lewis the undermanager was amongst the rescuers and unfortunately became a casualty.

The explosion at Naval Colliery on Sunday 27 January 1884 in the morning claimed the following fourteen miners' lives:

Names of casualties	Age	Occupation
1. Thomas Davies	46	contractor
2. Solomon Edwards	42	ostler
3. John Escott	27	ostler
4. John Heycock	42	fireman
5. John Heycock Jnr	19	collier
6. David Jones	52	fireman
7. Oliver John	33	ostler
8. Thomas Lewis	34	undermanager
9. Fred Nugent	44	ostler
10. John Price	43	fireman
11. James Seville	49	rescuer
12. Daniel Thomas	35	rescuer
13. Edward Watkins	35	rescuer
14. William Williams	61	fireman

On 16 September 1889 the accident reports show that thirty-eight-year-old collier James Price was killed underground by a fall of a slip of coal and clod 16ft in length and 4ft 6ins in thickness while he was holing below it without sprags. Two feet of coal were held above the timbers and this was used as the roof; on 22 September 1890 the accident reports show that forty-seven-year-old timberman James Lamb was killed underground when he was crushed between loaded drams on a parting after finishing his shift. On seeing some drams being let down a short distance, he jumped forward to pick up his measuring stick which was lying on the road and was caught by the drams; on 16 October 1890 the accident reports show that sixteen-year-old slummer Joseph Davies was injured by the cage which was descending upon him while he was attempting to cross the shaft. He worked ten days after the accident and died on the 2 January 1891; on 2 September 1891 the accident reports show that twenty-two-year-old collier Morgan Eales was killed underground on a self acting incline while he was riding on a loaded dram which had been sent away before the empty dram was attached at the bottom; on 23 September 1891 forty-nine-year-old collier Thomas Stephens was killed underground by a fall of a slip of coal which was overhanging and not spragged in the Four-Feet coal seam which was worked on the longwall system. The longwall system is a method of mining coal with all the colliers of that district manning one lengthy coalface, it would have been 'hand-got' earlier and machine cut later. No pillars of coal are left behind in a longwall face and the roof allowed to cave in behind the line of supports. Some faces would need intermediate packs if roof conditions were inferior. (Also called longwork, earlier.) On 23 April 1892 the accident reports show that twenty-two-year-old haulier Edwin Greese was killed underground when his head came in contact with a brow in the roof while riding on the shaft, the road was dipping and on 14 December 1895 the accident reports show that overman John Way, shoer William Rogers, striker Bertie Horton and striker Henry Avery

were killed when they fell out of the pit cage. Naval Colliery was closed with the Nantgwyn Colliery in October 1958 by the NCB.

New Risca Pit, Risca,
Sirhowy Valley, Monmouthshire

The New Risca Colliery was situated on the eastern side of the entrance to the Sirhowy Valley and was sunk in 1872 by the London and South Wales Colliery Co. The mine was sunk about 1,260 yards to the north-east and on the same coal seam as the Black Vein Colliery. Coal was first raised in June 1878. The two pits were separated by an extensive barrier of unworked coal. The colliery, according to one mine inspector, was well organised, and highly efficient, there being sufficient managers, deputies, overmen and firemen to maintain an adequate cover underground.

The mine was worked on a three-shift basis, each shift eight hours in duration; the two-day shifts were used to cut and haul out the coal while the third was used as a maintenance and preparation shift and was non-productive. For some time prior to the disaster, in which 119 men and boys and sixty-nine pit ponies lost their lives, the miners had misgivings about the recently introduced longwall method of extracting coal. They favoured the more traditional pillar and stall system. The men claimed that during the sixteen hours of productive mining, the face being worked advanced forward too fast and there was not enough time being allowed for the dispersal of dangerous accumulations of gas. Further concern was raised that insufficient timbers were being used to prop up the roof which was unstable. However, a 3ft layer of the residual coal had been left intact in an effort to support the roof. The management dismissed the miners' claims, pointing out that very few injuries had been reported as a result of roof falls.

Examinations of the workings following the disaster showed that a large roof fall had taken place; whether this had been caused by the blast or occurred prior to the explosion was never ascertained. The force of the blast was so great that the ventilating fan was extensively damaged and the rescuers, who had begun to assemble at the pit, were unable to enter the shaft because of the suspected high concentration of afterdamp.

All the bodies recovered had been badly burned. The first victim to be brought to the surface was searched by a police officer and his pocket watch had stopped at 1.30 a.m., exactly the time of the explosion. Recovery of the remaining victims proved to be a painfully slow process due to the numerous roof falls. It is probable that the explosion occurred as a result of a 'blower' (a blower is a sudden emission of firedamp in a mine). In contrast to other pit disasters, New Risca Colliery saw few grieving relatives assembled at the surface of the colliery. Those who had lost a relative in the explosion chose to shed their tears in the privacy of their own homes. However, Sunday saw the arrival of thousands of sightseers who invaded the stricken valley where so many men and boys had died.

Then began the official report issued by the Home Office. The report was a compilation of evidence given over a three-day period before a Coroner's court which was held in the nearby Cross Keys Inn on 24 August. Over forty witnesses were called to give evidence and detailed information gave fresh insight into the tragedy. The deputies, when inspecting the mine workings, utilised the Davy flame safety lamp. However, the colliers and labourers used the older type Clanny lamp. Near the bottom of the shaft naked flames were used, yet doubts had always been expressed at the wisdom of using the Clanny lamp. These doubts were echoed with the findings of the inquest. Originally designed in 1813, the Clanny lamp was the brainchild of

Dr William Reid Clanny, a native of Sutherland. His invention was regarded as being the first practical attempt to produce a safety lamp, which would ensure some measure of protection to miners in the dangerous confines underground at the pit. A series of improvements were made to the lamp's design and by 1839 his sixth attempt produced one whereby the flame was surrounded by a glass tube surmounted with a gauze cylinder and top. This added greatly to the illuminating power of the light. Sir Humphrey Davy was of the opinion that the unshielded gauze was potentially dangerous without some form of protection from strong air-currents, which might contain afterdamp. It was to be almost half a century later before his theory was proved correct.

However, there were no adequate means of testing the lamp's safety. Invariably, miners simply blew against the glass to see if the flame flickered. This was an indication that gas could, if present, reach the naked flame. The lamp was sealed at its base by an Indian rubber ring and much depended on this being properly fitted to ensure correct working. The force of the ventilation air passing through the workings was recorded as eight feet per second. Already it was known that a man walking against the current of air would greatly increase the velocity of the wind upon the lamp, creating a potentially dangerous situation. With the evidence pointing to a violent escape of gas added to the air passing through the pit, a lamp, if incorrectly sealed, would be capable of causing an explosion. This evidence led to the banning of the Clanny lamp in the mine.

Although bearing some burns, it was apparent that the majority of those who had died were victims of the explosion, but some did fall victim to the effects of carbonic acid gas. The lack of proper safety controls was so apparent that even the belief in the protection offered by the Clanny, a so-called safety lamp, was to prove both misguided, and in terms of human life, costly. They had seen their last sunset that filled the sky with a golden light above the misty valley.

The explosion at New Risca Colliery on Wednesday 15 July 1880 at 1.30 a.m. claimed the lives of the following 119 men and boys:

Names of casualties	Age	Names of casualties	Age
1. Henry Adams	45	22. John Daley	18
2. William Adams	50	23. James Davies	18
3. William Ashman	24	24. William Davies	34
4. Frederick Baker	17	25 .Samuel Dix	51
5. Henry Baker	24	26. Thomas Dix	26
6. Frederick Ball	36	37. Charles Edmunds	50
7. William Benn	42	28. Charles Edwards	50
8. Thomas Bowden	35	29. Daniel Edwards	48
9. David Brake	29	30. Thomas Edwards	24
10. John Bray	57	31. Uriah Edwards	37
11. Thomas Breeze	47	32. Mark Emery	29
12. Henry Brookman	40	33. Charles English	45
13. Stephen Bush	64	34. George Evans	55
14. William Bush	25	35. Joseph Everett	59
15. William Caines	68	36. Cornelius Ford	16
16. Charles Carey	26	37. Morgan Francis	32
17. William Charles	45	38. John Fry	28
18. Thomas Chiddy	29	39. Thomas Griffiths	38
19. William Cordey	49	40. Simon Gulliver	45
20. Mark Crook	30	41. Joseph Harley	33
21. Thomas Dale	46	42. Simon Harris	25

Names of casualties	Age	Names of casualties	Age
43. William Harris	25	82. William Palmer	66
44. Henry Harvey	41	83. William Phillips	34
45. Jarvis Harvey	13	84. Charles Poole	13
46. James Haycocks	25	85. George Poole	45
47. Evan Hayes	27	86. John Potter	29
48. William Hughs	43	87. John Powell	18
49. Jerry Hurley	22	88. Stephen Powell	26
50. John Hyatt	53	89. Thomas Price	32
51. Daniel James	39	90. Thomas Rendall	27
52. Daniel Jay	44	91. George Rosser	35
53. Jephtha Johnson	26	92. Jesse Sage	42
54. James Jones	20	93. David Scannell	43
55. John Jones	34	94. William Sheen	45
56. John Jones	27	95. Alfred Shore	13
57. Phillip Jones	26	96. George Smith	24
58. Thomas Jones	72	97. William John Stafford	13
59. Thomas Jones	60	98. Thomas Summerhill	24
60. Thomas Jones	25	99. Isaac Theophilus	40
61. William Leicester	19	100. Lewis Thomas	38
62. Thomas Lent	36	101. Thomas Thomas	36
63. Daniel Lewis	47	102. Henry Tooze	29
64. David Lewis	31	103. William James Tovey	13
65. Llewellyn Lewis	17	104. Samuel Tucker	35
66. Thomas Lewis	43	105. George Vaughan	55
67. William Lewis	20	106. William Vaughan	13
68. Lewis Leyshon	50	107. Thomas Wallace	52
69. Rees Leyshon	52	108. Thomas Wallace	17
70. William Lister	43	109. Thomas Walters	32
71. Robert Lugg	40	110. William West	41
72. Henry Marsh	19	111. Edward Wilcox	30
73. William Mathews	52	112. Lewis Williams	32
74. Charles Meade	38	113. Samuel Williams	35
75. William Mills	56	114. John Woodford	18
76. John Milson	20	115. Thomas Woolley	29
77. Henry Milson	35	116. -?--?-	
78. Daniel Moore	19	117. John Wynn	30
79. John Morgan	28	118. George Yemm	38
80. Thomas Morgan	17	119. Mesech Yemm	20
81. William Morgan	31		

The force of a further explosion on 15 January 1882 destroyed the pit head staging and damaged the ventilation fan blades and before a rescue attempt could be made precious time was spent on emergency repairs to the fan.

At the inquest it was stated that Charles Dixon was carrying 5lbs of dynamite to use underground for shotfiring but it could not be established whether he had charged or fired any shotholes.

The explosion at New Risca Colliery on Sunday 15 January 1882 in the morning claimed the following four miners' lives:

Names of casualties	Age	Occupation
1. Charles Dixon	44	overman
2. Francis Evans	38	fireman
3. John Gittings	41	fireman
4. Evan Morgan	28	labourer

New Risca Colliery was closed on 9 July 1966 by the NCB.

New Tredegar Colliery, New Tredegar, Rhymney Valley, Glamorganshire

New Tredegar Colliery (the Moving Mountain Pit also known locally as the Old Pits) was sunk by Thomas Powell in 1854. The two shafts were 345 yards deep but one of them was exclusively used for pumping mine water. Ventilation was by a Struve fan which was in use at Black Vein Colliery, Risca in 1860, a system not greatly favoured by Mr Lionel Brough, the chief inspector of that year. Coal seams worked were the Big Vein and Yard. On 12 November 1860 the accident reports show that forty-five-year-old labourer William Shellard was seriously injured by an explosion of firedamp; he died on the 28 November 1860. The masons were walling a trial pit sunk near the bottom of the pumping shaft, when one of the men took off the gauze of his lamp, which exploded the gas and the scaffold was upset and they all fell to the bottom of the shaft. On 3 June 1872 the accident reports show that thirteen-year-old trapper Thomas James was killed underground when he was crushed by a journey of drams. On 4 December 1875 at approximately 8.30 a.m. there came a fearful blast from the shaft and it was said to have emptied every house in the village. The rescue party led by the manager Mr Robert Lonnie found that the area underground in the vicinity of the explosion had little damage.

The explosion at New Tredegar Colliery on Sunday 4 December claimed the following twenty-three men and boys' lives:

Names of casualties	Names of casualties
1. John Davies	13. Thomas Price
2. Arthur Edwards	14. Jonathan Richards
3. Ethan Edwards	15. George Saunders
4. Thomas Evans	16. Stephan Sellick
5. William Evans	17. Arthur Thomas
6. Edward Hinder	18. John Thomas
7. James James	19. George Williams
8. Samuel Jenkins	20. John Williams
9. John Jones	21. Roger Williams
10. John Jones	22. Thomas J. Williams
11. Llewellyn Jones	23. William Williams
12. Moses Prangley	

On 7 July 1884 the accident reports show that fifty-two-year-old hitcher John Jones was killed when a lump of coal fell off the cage which had just landed at the surface and bounced off the top of the cage at pit bottom and struck him. On 5 November 1884 the accident reports show

that thirty-five-year-old haulier William Johnson was injured underground by a fall of stone. He died on 19 November 1894. New Tredegar Colliery was abandoned in the 1920s.

Oakwood Colliery, Llynfi Valley, Glamorganshire

Oakwood Colliery was opened and owned by William Davies in 1864 and was also known locally as Pwll Davies (Davies Pit). The colliery was also owned by Elders Navigation Collieries Limited from 1899, Celtic Collieries Limited from 1909 and North's Navigation Collieries (1889) Limited from 1920 until its closure. The manpower in 1922 was 250. On 25 March 1868 the accident reports show that eighteen-year-old collier Jonathan Morris was killed underground by a journey of drams. Oakwood Colliery was closed in 1929.

Old Castle Colliery, Near Llanelli, Carmarthenshire

Old Castle Colliery was opened by Williams, Neville & Co. in 1867. On 18 June 1872 the accident reports show that fifty-four-year-old collier William Johns was killed underground by a fall of roof and on 8 July 1872 the accident reports show that twenty-three-year-old trammer Joshua Thomas was killed underground by a fall of roof. Old Castle Colliery was abandoned in 1887.

Old Pit, Blaina, Ebbw Fach Valley, Monmouthshire

Old Pit, Blaina was opened by Levick & Simpson in 1858. On 18th March 1860 the accident reports show that twenty-six-year-old collier Thomas Jones was killed underground by a fall of Elled (coal seam) roof, which broke over the timber, but some dangerous slips and joints then became exhibited. Old Pit, Blaina was abandoned in 1922.

Old Pit, Gadlys, Cynon Valley, Glamorganshire

Old Pit was sunk in 1802 and was then locally known as the New Pit and the Victoria Pit and was sunk to a depth of 80 yards. Old Pit was owned by Gadlys Iron Co. in 1853. On 6 January 1853 the accident reports show that forty-nine-year-old collier Samuel Franklin was killed when he fell down the pit; on 29 November 1853 the accident reports show that forty-seven-year-old collier John Williams was fatally injured; on 26 January 1860 the accident reports show that twenty-four-year-old haulier Evan Davies was killed underground by a fall of roof in the Four-Feet coal seam; on 2 February 1860 twelve-year-old doorboy Thomas Jones was killed underground. At approximately 2.30 a.m. on 4 October 1871 an explosion killed four miners. A horse was also killed and another one badly burnt at the head and neck and was so weak it had to be helped to its stall on the surface. Great tenderness was witnessed towards the poor horse; on 19 December 1873 the accident reports show that twenty-six-year-old roadman John Evans was killed underground and on 5 August 1874 the accident reports show that twelve-year-old doorboy T. Prichard was killed underground by a fall of stone.

The explosion at Old Pit, Gadlys on Sunday 4 December 1871 claimed the following four men and boys' lives:

Names of casualties	Age
1. David Davies	27
2 .Thomas Hamlett	11
3. David Jones	28
4. David Morse	18

Old Pit, Gadlys was closed in 1902 by Wayne's Merthyr Collieries.

Old Coal Pit, Blaenavon, Afon Lwyd Valley, Monmouthshire

Old Coal Pit was opened by Blaenavon Iron Co. in 1876. On 24 March 1868 the accident reports show that twenty-five-year-old collier David Jenkins was killed underground by a piece of clod from the roof which suddenly fell and killed him. The face of his work should have been cropped (pulled down). Old Coal Pit was abandoned in 1898.

Parc Slip Colliery, Fountain, Aberkenfig, Glamorganshire

When he knocked on the door, his mother thought she had seen a ghost.
Parc Slip Drift Mine was opened by the Llynfi, Tondu and Ogmore Coal and Iron Co. Ltd in 1875. On 13 October 1868 the accident reports show that twenty-three-year-old timberman W. Baker was killed underground by a dram which fell on him while ascending; on 9 July 1873 the accident reports show that twenty-two-year-old collier James John was killed underground by a fall of roof; on 15 January 1876 fifty-year-old collier Joseph Watkins was killed underground by a fall of coal and on 8 April 1884 the accident reports show that thirty-one-year-old collier William Howell and forty-eight-year-old collier Thomas Jones were killed underground by an explosion of firedamp.

On Friday 26 August 1892 at 8.30 a.m. 112 men and boys died in the explosion of firedamp at Parc Slip Colliery, near the Fountain, Aberkenfig, owned by North's Navigation Collieries (1889) Limited. This was without doubt one of the most important as well as tragic events in the history of the locality. Of the thirty-nine others who came out alive, some bore both physical and emotional scars. The victims left behind them over 200 dependants, widows, children and elderly parents.

For a period of about ten days the whole neighbourhood must have been steeped in communal gloom as the dead bodies were gradually and laboriously retrieved, and as multiple funerals hurried through the sombre streets towards one or other of the burial grounds, Saint John's, Llansantffraid, Smyrna, Nebo, Siloam, where graves had been prepared, sometimes row upon row. The first payments were made out of the relief funds; some families needed assistance even with burial expenses. The domestic devastation is hard as well as painful to imagine. More than one father had died with his son or sons; two, three or even four brothers in one family had met their deaths together. One woman lost her father, husband and brother. No aspect of social life was left untouched. Schools were suspended as pupils stayed away, and churches and chapels found it all but impossible to continue with services where attempts at singing were choked by tears.

It was two months after the disaster before the last bodies were retrieved, the last victim (George Dunster) being laid to rest in Saint John's churchyard on 2 November. The repercussions of the tragedy must, however, be measured in years rather than months. For nearly sixty years afterwards, payments continued to be made out of the Relief Fund, albeit to a steadily diminishing band of dependants; the fund was wound up in April 1950, when the names of only two dependants remained on the books.

After several years in the ownership of North's Navigation, Friday 26 August promised, in the anticipation of many, to be a day of pleasure, for it was the day of the annual Saint Mary Hill Fair. The fair was only too often spoiled by bad weather, but this time the previous couple of days had been fine and Friday, too, dawned bright with promise. Some colliers had changed shifts to go to the fair and altogether there was a good deal of pleasant bustling about to be done as excited families sat down to breakfast or prepared for the day's outing. The fun of the fair came to an abrupt halt as the thunderous roar of the massive explosion rent the air. As the ground shook beneath them from the blast four miles distant, the hearts of the holidaying crowds were suddenly filled with terror. Miner Ned Jones knew the explosion meant his twelve-year-old son was in grave danger. David Jones of Cae Ceddau, Litchard Hill, Bridgend, had been due to go to Saint Mary Hill Fair with his father that sunny late-summer day. But, in a fateful decision, he opted to go to work at the pit instead. As he heard the sound of the explosion, Ned leapt into the saddle of his horse and galloped to the Parc Slip Colliery where he and his son worked. It was already too late. David was one of the 112 men and boys killed in the disaster. His nephew, Wyndham Parry John of Llangeinor, said, 'He was supposed to go with his dad to the fair, but changed his mind'. A great friend of his father's told him not to worry, saying, 'I will look after him, Ned'. 'Don't' worry, Ned, he's safe in my arms'. When David was found, his father's friend had been as good as his word. His arms were wrapped around him trying to shield him from the explosion. 'The explosion was heard by Uncle Ned at Saint Mary Hill. He knew it was Parc Slip. He mounted his horse and galloped to Parc Slip. The horse dropped dead as he dismounted at the colliery'. Ned Jones struggled to come to terms with the guilt associated with his son's death. 'He used to tell my mam, "It was my fault, Sarah, I should have made him come with me"', said Wyndham John.

Parc Slip was in many ways the least typical of the major pit disasters of the late nineteenth century. The mine was a relatively small one, employing 200 men and previously had a good safety record in an area not noted for fiery or gassy pits. It was also a drift mine, in which a tunnel led into a hillside, descending gently to the coalface. Most of the danger of the coal industry has been associated with deep mining. Parc Slip, which left sixty women widowed and 153 children fatherless, also became notable for the number of people who got out of it alive. Because the explosion had occurred deep in the bowels of the pit, it was thought that no one working at the coalface would survive. But a series of dramatic rescues succeeded in getting aid and fresh air to the men who had huddled in the darkness for days rather than venture out through the poison-filled tunnels. A total of forty-one men were recovered alive from the pit, although some of the rescuers, like James Bowen, lost their own lives trying to bring them to safety. James Bowen was one of the true heroes of the Parc Slip disaster. For there is little doubt that, but for his selfless actions and strong leadership in the wake of the explosion, many more men would have died there. But his brave attempts to get help to his colleagues cost Mr Bowen his own life. Two of his sons also perished in the blast, although a third walked out of the pit alive after nearly a week underground. Mr Bowen was in charge of a gang of twenty-two men at the coalface at the number four stage of the pit. He attempted to lead the nineteen who survived the immediate aftermath of the blast to safety. They reached an area of the mine known as the East Turn, but here Mr Bowen stopped. He explained to the rest of the men that the safest course of action would be to stay where they were while he went to get help. 'Some of his companions argued against this, while others offered to go with him but he remained firm, and being the man of authority they obeyed', recalled an eyewitness in a contemporary newspaper report of the tragedy. Mr Bowen left the gang of men about midday on Friday. Another rescue party discovered his lifeless body later that night. Mr Bowen's sons Jason, sixteen, and Thomas, fourteen, who also died are buried with their father in Penyfai churchyard. But a third son, Levi, was one of the miners who survived the blast, returning as if from the grave. 'They had given him up for dead but he walked out a week later', said granddaughter Mrs Walters. 'When he knocked on the door, his mother thought she had seen a ghost'.

The Parc Slip disaster of 1892 was the worst to hit the small close-knit mining communities and still looms large in the history of the area. The explosion claimed the lives of the following 112 men and boys:

Names of casualties
1. Thomas Baker
2. Henry Barnett
3. James Berwick
4. John Berwick
5. David Bowen
6. James Bowen
7. Jason Bowen
8. Thomas Bowen
9. Moses Bromham
10. Alfred Burrows
11. Thomas Carter
12. John Chapel
13. John Cockram
14. George Cockram
15. Lewis Cockram
16. Thomas Cockram
17. John Curtin
18. Thomas Daniels
19. David David
20. Evan David
21. Phillip David
22. Benjamin Davies
23. David Davies
24. David Davies
25. Enoch Davies

Names of casualties
26. George Davies
27. James Davies
28. Richard Davies
29. Richard Davies
30. William Davies
31. Edward Down
32. Elijah Driscoll
33. John Driscoll
34. George Dunster
35. John Dunster
36. George Edwards
37. James Evans
38. John Gibbon
39. James Gibbs
40. John Hanley
41. Jonathan Hanley
42. David Harry
43. George Henson
44. Thomas Henson
45. David Hopkin
46. Evan Hopkins
47. Thomas Hopkins
48. Thomas Hopkins
49. Elias Howell
50. Elias Howell

51. Edward Humphreys
52. Henry Hurley
53. George Jacobs
54. Thomas Jacobs
55. Jenkin Jenkins
56. John John
57. David Jones
58. David Jones
59. David Jones
60. Evan Jones
61. Thomas Jones
62. John Lovell
63. George Lowman
64. Thomas Lukins
65. Albert Lyddon
66. George Lyddon
67. Henry Lyddon
68. Herbert Lyddon
69. James Lyddon
70. William Lyddon
71. David Major
72. Arthur Martin
73. H. Mitchell
74. Evan Morgan
75. Lewis Morgan
76. .Morgan Morgan
77. William Morris
78. Charles Nichols
79. James Orchard
80. John Osborne
81. Joseph Painter

82. .W.J. Painter
83. David Powell snr
84. David Powell jnr
85. Thomas Rees
86. James Richards
87. Frederick Roberts
88. Griffith Roberts
89. John Roberts
90. John Rosser
91. William Rosser
92. Herbert Saunders
93. Charles Stenner
94. Thomas Stenner
95. William Stenner
96. Henry Strike
97. George Tackle
98. Thomas Taylor
99. David Thomas
100. Ivor Thomas
101. John Thomas
102. Rees Thomas
103. Christopher Warren
104. R.H. Webster snr
105. R.H. Webster jnr
106. Thomas Webster
107. Gwilym Williams
108. Thomas Williams
109. Thomas Williams
110. Thomas Williams
111. William Williams
112. William Williams

The verdict was accidental death.

Parc Slip Drift Mine was closed in 1904 by North's Navigation Collieries Limited.

Park Colliery, Cwmparc, Rhondda Valley, Glamorganshire

Sinking began at the Park Colliery in 1864 by David Davies and Co. In 1935 the Park Colliery became part of the Powell Duffryn Steam Coal Co. and the colliery was acquired by the National Coal Board in 1947. The coal seams worked were the Two-Feet-Nine, Lower-Six-Feet, Upper-Nine-Feet, Lower-Nine-Feet, Bute, Yard, Upper-Seven-Feet, Five-Feet and the Gellideg. On 13 October 1868 the accident reports show that thirty-three-year-old collier David Richards was killed underground by a fall of stone; on 15 June 1872 the accident reports show that fifty-eight-year-old furnaceman William Davies was killed by being drawn up to the sheave. A person named William Thomas, who was insane, got into the engine-house and started the engine and could not stop it; on 3 February 1876 the accident reports show that fifty-year-old collier J. Lewis was killed underground by a fall of stone; on 1 March 1876 the accident reports show that twenty-two-year-old hitcher Jonathan Israel was killed by getting under the cage at the bottom of the shaft and on 20 July 1876 the accident reports show that labourer W. Williams was killed by trucks. Park Colliery was closed in February 1966 by the NCB.

Pochin Colliery, Near Tredegar, Sirhowy Valley, Monmouthshire

Pochin Colliery was sunk in 1876 by the Tredegar Iron Co. It was abandoned for four years and finally completed in 1880. Coal seams worked were the Big Coal, Yard, Meadow Vein and Upper Rhas Las. On 8 August 1884 at 9.10 p.m. an explosion killed fourteen miners and forty-three pit ponies. In 1954 with a manpower of 693 it produced an annual output of 152,000 tons of coal.

The explosion at Pochin Colliery on Saturday 8 August 1884 claimed the following fourteen miners' lives:

Names of casualties	Age	Occupation
1. James Bevan	39	labourer
2. John Davies	46	roadman
3. William Evans	30	collier
4. Evan Griffiths	20	collier
5. John Hammer	35	collier
6. William Havard	25	haulier
7. John Jones	25	haulier
8. Thomas Lewis	35	labourer
9. Thomas Morgan	34	collier
10. Isaiah Morris	28	roadman
11. Gwilym Owen	34	collier
12. James Preece	34	labourer
13. William Scott	48	labourer
14. John Williams	20	collier

Pochin Colliery was closed on Saturday 25 July 1964 by the NCB.

Prince of Wales Colliery, Abercarn, Ebbw Fawr Valley, Monmouthshire

Prince of Wales Colliery was opened in 1836 by the Abercarn Coal Co.; other owners included Ebbw Vale Steel, Iron and Coal Co. and United National Collieries. Coal seams worked were the Black Vein, Old Coal and the Rock Vein. On 12 May 1853 the accident reports show that miner William Thomas was killed underground by a fall of roof; on 26 June 1872 the accident reports show that thirty-one-year-old haulier Thomas Weal was killed underground when he fell under a dram; on 2 August 1872 the accident reports show that forty-eight-year-old collier Thomas Morgan was killed underground by an explosion of firedamp and on 11 September 1878 an explosion killed 268 men and boys and fifty-seven pit ponies. Twenty-seven years after the incident, miners found a complete skeleton in ragged clothing and boots. At the inquest it was held that he was one of the victims and unidentifiable.

A loud booming sound echoed around the hillsides above Abercarn. The tremor which followed brought the villagers to their front doors; all eyes were on the pit. A plume of dense, billowing smoke crept menacingly around the headgear of the colliery. The shrill of the pit hooter shocked the still morning air. It verified their worst anxieties: problems underground. With hats, coats and shawls hastily thrown on, the villagers hurried to the colliery. Before the day was out, every family in the community would be touched by the grief of losing a loved one; the valley flowed with heartbreaking tears.

Volunteers assembled, all ready to descend into the pit, despite the danger that lay hidden beneath. Those brought up the pit told of the serious situation below. Cage after cage was raised, and with each arrival came more survivors, many suffering horrific injuries. Having brought to safety all those who had made their way to the shaft, the rescue teams entered the mine. Progress was painfully slow, thick smoke swirled around them. The coal and timber of the workings were ablaze. To add to their difficulties the air was filled with the acrid stench of deadly afterdamp. They battled their way forward over the debris.

A short distance from the shaft the rescue party came across fifty-seven badly burned pit ponies. All had died in the blast that had swept through the mine. Disregarding their own safety, and close to exhaustion, the miners struggled through the heat and choking fumes of a living nightmare. Desperate and frustrated in their attempts to bring out any of their comrades who might have survived the catastrophe, they laboured on.

The greatness of the task before them was so grave. By evening only eighty-two of the total workforce of 350 had been brought to the surface alive. Those who had died amid the fury of explosion lay deep inside the labyrinth of tunnels. Finally, faced by the rapidly deteriorating conditions, and fearful of another explosion, the rescuers were recalled, having recovered only seven bodies. It was decided that a further attempt to reach those still underground would be made the following morning.

For those who waited at the top of the pit throughout the long hours of darkness the grey, cold valley morning brought renewed hope and another rescue attempt was made but the conditions underground had not improved and hope of finding any other survivors was abandoned.

One miner who lived through this terrible ordeal recalled:

We stopped and listened, other men came up to join us, and we stood there, fifteen in number, something was wrong. The air was getting bad, and we began to make our way to the shaft. Presently we came to a door, there was a gaping hole in it allowing the air to come through, and it was blowing hard. Someone said 'if you try to get out that way you will be blown down'. But I stepped to one side and climbed through, the others followed. Further along we came upon a man who was on his hands and knees, he wasn't dead, but we knew he was dying. Then we found another, and still more, all were on their hands and knees. The gas was very strong here and we straggled on staggering like drunken men, our caps pressed to our mouths. Finally we reached better air, and we knew that we had reached the bottom of the shaft. As I reached the bottom I fell over the body of a dead horse and lost my light. There was quite a crowd of us, some were on fire, burning and shouting out. There were some dead and others dying. Those who were injured lay groaning, or crying aloud. Some men were calling to one another; there was such a noise that you couldn't hear yourself speak. About seventy or eighty of us crowded into that small place, all looking up at the spot of light above us, that looked like a star. The signals were broken, and the guide ropes were all down. It was impossible to get silence amid the clamour and fear all round. At last it grew quiet. Someone struck a piece of iron with his mandril, the noise spiralling up to the surface. The signal was understood and the cage came down. Down it came and, oh, the fight there was to get in it! No one knew if another explosion might happen at any moment, and every soul be crushed. Up went the cage, the next time it come down a ladder was sent with it. Such was the struggle to get in, I can tell you, that the ladder was broken in two. On the next journey down a longer ladder was sent, with this one we managed better. I came up with the third cage full of men. I was thankful to see the sun and breathe fresh air.

Faced with abandoning the expected rescue attempt, those whose loved ones were still numbered amongst the missing were outraged. Calls for another descent and the continued search for survivors were made. But the dangers of an imminent and more violent explosion were so great that permission to carry out another rescue was refused. Officials, including the management and Mr Thomas Cadman the mines inspector, reasoned that lives would be put needlessly at risk. Utter despair fell upon those who had waited, prayed and hoped throughout that endless night. Now, all that was left for them was the recovery and Christian burial of the bodies.

Following the explosion, a party of mining engineers went down the Cwmcarn shaft to examine its condition. Whilst making their way along the tunnels they came upon twelve bodies. Removal of the victims began, when the alarm was raised concerning the high level of firedamp in the surrounding area. Fearing another explosion at any moment, the dead were left where they lay and the engineers returned quickly to the surface. The shaft at Cwmcarn was sealed to prevent air from feeding the fire.

Government mine inspectors along with the colliery managers debated on what course of action should next be taken. After much soul-searching it was agreed that the mine should be flooded using water from the nearby Monmouthshire Canal. The colliery had been flooded in an incident on a previous occasion and this time such a decision was greeted by a public outcry. Had it not been bad enough that the men and boys of Abercarn had to perish at the hands of explosion, fire and poisonous gas? Now their lifeless bodies were to be tormented further by the torrents of canal water that would pour into the pit. By nightfall the muddy canal waters had been channelled to the shaft and the slow process of flooding the network of subterranean passages began. It was two months later and not until some 35 million gallons of water had been used that engineers were satisfied that the raging fires were under control. The task of draining the pit of such a vast quantity of water began on 9 November and the slow process was to take twenty-five days of continual pumping. However, no sooner had work commenced, than the pumps became blocked with the debris from the pit bottom. In an effort to resolve the matter the Royal Navy sent divers from Newport who successfully managed to free the pumps. Eventually the water level was reduced sufficiently to allow a rescue team below ground to begin the grisly task of recording the dead.

The inquest into the disaster proved a lengthy affair. Evidence showed that overall the mine was well-managed and had a good safety record. The conclusion of the mine inspector's report was that the explosion was probably caused by the ignition of gas by means of a flame safety lamp. During the course of the hearing, many commendations for bravery were cited.

About two months after the dreadful explosion the bodies of fifty victims had still not been recovered. The Ebbw Vale Co. in a report to the Home Secretary said that its resources had been so badly strained by the explosion that it could not finance further remedial work at the pit. The Ebbw Vale Co. was reminded of the duties imposed upon it by the terms of its lease and by public opinion. This gentle pressure must have been effective for in 1882 the colliery resumed production.

The explosion at Prince of Wales Colliery on Wednesday 11 September 1878 claimed the following 268 men and boys' lives:

Names of casualties	Age	Occupation
1. George Abraham	16	collier
2. Richard Abraham	14	doorboy
3. Thomas Abraham	37	collier
4. George Adams	19	collier
5. William Allen	29	haulier
6. David Anthony	16	collier
7. William Arnold	23	collier
8. Thomas Ashman	33	collier
9. Charles Baker	30	collier
10. John Bakerton	26	shackler
11. Isaac Bath	21	collier
12. David Beachy	16	collier
13. John Beak	24	hitcher
14. James Beard	52	collier
15. John Beard	21	labourer
16. William Bennett	21	collier
17. Edwin Bethel	48	undermanager
18. Morgan Boden	32	collier
19. George Brooks	24	shackler
20. Frederick Brown	25	collier
21. James Brown	27	repairer
22. William Brown	14	light carrier
23. Henry Budd	19	haulier
24. Joseph Cains	45	lampman
25. Frederick Carlton	18	collier
26. John Carter	22	collier
27. William Carter	19	haulier
28. Henry Cartwright	43	collier
29. Herbert Cartwright	16	collier
30. Frederick Chaddick	33	collier
31. John Chapman	35	collier
32. Frederick Chin	22	collier
33. Joseph Clifford	27	collier
34. William Clifford	18	collier
35. John Cocker	46	collier
36. George Coles	48	collier
37. John Colley	52	collier
38. William Colley	16	collier
39. Henry Cooksey	26	collier
40. George G. Coombs	26	collier
41. Benjamin Coward	38	collier
42. Charles Cridland	26	rider
43. John Cridland	52	lampman
44. John Daniel	25	haulier

45. Alfred Davies	18	collier
46. David Davies	40	shackler
47. David Davies	21	collier
48. Edwin Davies	23	collier
49. Henry Davies	29	collier
50. James Davies	29	haulier
51. John Davies	47	repairer
52. Thomas Davies	35	haulier
53. Thomas Davies	16	collier
54. William Davies	48	master haulier
55. William Davies jnr	18	haulier
56. William H. Davies snr	15	collier
57. Frederick Doel	30	collier
58. Henry Down	28	collier
59. William Downs	24	collier
60. George Eatwell	29	collier
61. John Edwards	26	haulier
62. John Edwards	25	collier
63. William Edwards	48	collier
64. Griffiths England	38	collier
65. David Evans	21	haulier
66. Edwin Evans	14	collier's boy
67. George Evans	50	collier
68. Gwilym Evans	18	ropesmith
69. John Evans	43	collier
70. John Evans	24	collier
71. Thomas Evans	40	collier
72. John Everett	36	collier
73. John Franks	43	collier
74. Benjamin Games	25	engineman
75. John Games	33	collier
76. William Games	35	collier
77. Elisha Gay	14	doorboy
78. Joseph Gay	45	overman
79. Henry Gillingham	36	collier
80. George Gleade	25	haulier
81. Gilbert Gleade	22	haulier
82. Henry Golding	34	hitcher
83. John Gough	15	haulier
84. Charles Greenland	22	collier
85. David Griffiths	26	haulier
86. James Griffiths	37	collier
87. John Hall	35	ostler
88. James Hancock	40	collier
89. William Harlaw	26	collier
90. Arthur Harris	16	collier
91. James Harris	30	fireman
92. John Harris	14	doorboy

93. John Havard	38	collier
94. Thomas Haycock	22	repairer
95. George Helburn	31	collier
96. William Helburn	39	collier
97. Oliver Hibbs	35	collier
98. John Hodges snr	47	collier
99. John Hodges jnr	18	collier
100. Joseph Hooper	13	haulier
101. William Hooper	15	collier's boy
102. William Hopper	27	hitcher
103. Rees Howells	39	collier
104. William Howells	25	collier
105 .David James	30	collier
106 .Lewis James	14	collier's boy
107. Rowland James	32	collier
108. William James	25	collier
109. Edward Jenkins	24	haulier
110. John Jenkins	50	collier
111. Henry C. Jennings	14	doorboy
112. Charles Jones	33	collier
113. David Jones	35	master haulier
114. Edmund Jones	18	collier
115. Joseph Jones	25	collier
116. Nathaniel Jones	22	hitcher
117. Solomon Jones	35	collier
118. Thomas Jones	57	collier
119. William Jones	38	collier
120. William Jones	26	haulier
121. William Jones	20	haulier
122. Joseph Jordan	21	foreman
123. Henry Knight	33	collier
124. William Lagg	15	collier's boy
125. John Lee	24	collier
126. Israel Lewis	34	repairer
127. John Lewis	31	haulier
128. John Lewis	20	master haulier
129. Joseph Lewis	25	repairer
130. Joseph Lewis	16	collier
131. Thomas Lewis	14	collier's boy
132. William Lewis	38	master haulier
133 .William Lewis	26	collier
134. George Lloyd	36	collier
135. James Lovell	34	collier
136. Isaac Madly	22	haulier
137. William Marshall	32	collier
138. Isaac Mathews	50	labourer
139. John Mathews	40	collier
140. John Mathews	23	collier

141. John McCarthy	21	collier
142. George Meredith	36	collier
143. Henry Meredith	16	collier
144. William Meyrick	32	shackler
145. Charles Moore	16	collier
146. Joseph Moore	14	collier's boy
147. Thomas Morgan	20	collier
148. William Morgan	38	collier
149. William Morgan	21	collier
150. Samuel Morton	40	collier
151. Charles Nealms	22	collier
152. Thomas Nealms	25	collier
153. John Newbury	30	collier
154. Charles Nicholas	18	ostler
155. Elias Nicholas	20	collier
156. Henry Nicholas	14	sweeper
157. Thomas Noot	48	collier
158. Thomas Noot snr	16	collier
159. Robert Noots jnr	14	doorboy
160. George Osborne	23	collier
161. Robert Osborne	21	collier
162. Henry Owen	21	collier
163. George Oxford	23	collier
164. George Pain	14	light carrier
165. James Pain	16	haulier
166. Thomas Palmer	22	collier
167. William Palmer	26	collier
168. Uriah Parry	20	collier
169. Thomas Phillips	25	collier
170. Thomas Phillips	34	haulier
171. Thomas Phillips	47	fireman
172. Thomas Phillips	21	ostler
173. Thomas Phillips	20	haulier
174. Thomas Phillips	13	doorboy
175. William Phillips	16	haulier
176. William Phillips	16	haulier
177. James Poelry	21	collier
178. Henry Portray	19	collier
179. Henry Powell	14	haulier
180. Samuel Powell	13	sweeper
181. James Price	15	collier's boy
182. William Price	26	collier
183. Henry Quick	28	collier
184. James Quick	21	collier
185. Joseph Railton	22	collier
186. David Rees	37	overman
187. David Rees	19	haulier
188. John Rees	39	collier

189. John Regan	19	haulier
190. John Regan	50	oilier
191. Michael Regan	23	haulier
192. John Reynolds	22	collier
193. Richard Richards	56	ostler
194. Thomas Rogers	29	collier
195. William Rogers	35	collier
196. John Rowe	42	collier
197. Henry Saunders	15	collier's boy
198. Richard Saunders	37	collier
199. George Shepherd	35	collier
200. Isaac Shepherd	40	repairer
201. James Smith	14	collier
202. Silas Smith	38	collier
203. Thomas Smith	30	collier
204. William Snelgrove	23	labourer
205. Frederick Stephens	14	collier's boy
206. John Stephens	16	collier
207. Richard Stephens	34	collier
208. William Stone	29	repairer
209. Albert J. Symonds	13	doorboy
210. Edward Symonds	35	repairer
211. Thomas Symonds	17	collier
212. William Symonds	39	collier
213. William H. Symonds	14	collier's boy
214. Augustus Thomas	23	collier
215. David Thomas	37	collier
216. David Thomas	21	collier
217. David Thomas	24	collier
218. William J. Thomas	28	haulier
219. Henry Terrill	47	fireman
220. Henry Tyrell	34	collier
221. Samuel Tyrell	13	doorboy
222. William H. Tyrell	15	collier's boy
223. William Tyrell	18	ropesmith
224. Thomas Tyler	38	collier
225. Henry Walters	18	shackler
226. Thomas Walters snr	66	collier
227. Thomas Walters jnr	25	collier
228. Thomas Walters	38	collier
229. William Warmouth	22	collier
230. Albert Watkins	20	roadman
231. Sydney Watkins	16	collier
232. Thomas Watkins	23	shackler
233. George Watts	31	collier
234. Henry Watts	30	collier
235. Isaac Watts	28	collier
236. Job Webb	55	collier

237. Thomas Webb	14	collier
238. Alfred Wells	36	collier
239. Alfred Wells	14	sweeper
240. Frank Whatley	13	doorboy
241. James Whatley	23	collier
242. William Whatley	26	labourer
243. Thomas Wicks	24	collier
244. Albert Wilcox	23	ropesmith
245. Daniel Williams	51	collier
246. Daniel Williams	59	collier
247. Edmund Williams	17	collier
248. Edward Williams	19	collier
249. Edwin Williams	14	doorboy
250. Henry Williams	22	collier
251. Isaac Williams	30	collier
252. Jacob Williams	33	repairer
253. John Williams	14	haulier
254. John Williams	35	collier
255. John Williams	30	collier
256. Jonathan Williams	14	collier's boy
257. Jonathan Williams	22	collier
258. Richard Williams	28	collier
259. Thomas Williams	16	repairer
260. Thomas Williams	37	collier
261. Thomas Williams	35	collier
262. Thomas Williams	43	collier
263. William Williams	45	labourer
264. William Williams	16	collier
265. William Williams	13	rider
266. William J. Williams	16	haulier
267. Aaron Winters	14	collier's boy
268. William Young	41	roadman

There were eighty-two miners brought out alive:

Names of survivors	Occupation	Names of survivors	Occupation
1. David Absalom	collier	13. Alfred Coombs	collier
2. James Absalom	collier	14. David Davies	repairer
3. Thomas Alsop	collier	15. James Davies	collier
4. William Anthony	collier	16. John Davies	collier
5. George Ashman	master haulier	17. John Davis	collier
6. John Baker	collier	18. William Davies	collier
7. Joseph Bassett	collier	19. William Davies	collier
8. Israel Bateman	collier	20. William Davies	haulier
9. Thomas Bryan	collier	21. James Dobbs	collier
10. George Carter	collier	22. William Dobbs	collier
11. Henry Carter	collier	23. John Drew	collier
12. Lemuel Charles	collier	24. Thomas Edmunds	collier

25. Thomas Eatwell	collier		54. George Moon	collier
26. Richard Edwards	collier		55. James Morgan	collier
27. John Evans	collier		56. John Morgan	doorboy
28. John Evans	collier		57. Morgan Morgan	collier
29. John Fletcher	collier		58. Roger Morgan	collier
30. Thomas Games	collier		59. Thomas Morgan	collier
31. John George	collier		60. James Nicholas	collier
32. William Gerrish	collier		61. Thomas Osborn	greaser
33. Thomas Goodey	collier		62. John Owen	collier
34. Morgan Griffiths	collier		63. Thomas Powell	collier
35. Hezekiah Harvey	collier		64. William Pritchard	collier
36. James Haycock	haulier		65. William Prosser	collier
37. Edward Haynes	collier		66. Michael Richards	repairer
38. Benjamin James	collier		67. Charles Roberts	collier
39. William Jenkins	collier		68. Emanuel Sheppard	collier
40. Daniel Jones	collier		69. Seth Sheppard	collier
41. John Jones	collier		70. Thomas Smith	collier
42. Jonah Jones	collier		71. James Stead	collier
43. N.H. Jones	collier		72. John Sweet	collier
44. Thomas Jones	collier		73. Samuel Toplass	collier
45. John Jordan	engineman		74. Thomas Waters	collier
46. John Knight	collier		75. Jonah Watkins	collier
47. John Lavender	collier		76. William West	collier
48. David Lewis	collier		77. William West	collier
49. George Lewis	collier		78. James Williams	collier
50. Henry Lewis	collier		79. John Williams	collier
51. Charles Mansfield	mason		80. Richard Williams	rider
52. William Mansfield	mason		81. Thomas Williams	collier
53. Thomas Meredith	collier		82. William Williams	collier

On 31 July 1884 the accident reports show that forty-seven-year-old labourer James Ledwitch was injured on the colliery surface when he fell off a plank near the boilers and hit his head. He died the next day; on 15 February 1886 the accident reports show that collier William Miles was killed underground by a fall of top coal. A slant was found running along the face. The manager told him to be cautious and he at once proceeded to set a prop, but before he erected the prop the coal fell and killed him; on 7 May 1886 the accident reports show that forty-two-year-old collier Thomas Jones was killed underground by a fall of coal. He was putting up a cog under the top coal when a large piece of coal fell owing to two large natural slips at right angles to each other, which were invisible. His work place was sufficiently timbered; on 4 May 1889 the accident reports show that a fourteen-year-old door boy F. Thomas Daniel was killed underground when he was blocked between a journey of drams in a parting in an engine plane; on 3 February 1891 the accident reports show that twenty-nine-year-old hitcher Lewis Davies was killed when a piece of coal fell down the shaft, as a full dram was being banked, and struck him. It is a wonder that this is not a more prolific source of accidents in South Wales seeing how the drams are loaded; on 22 April 1891 the accident reports show that thirty-year-old timberman John Soward was killed underground by a fall a roof. He was assisting a timberman in enlarging a heading which was crushed and while his comrade was preparing timber for

setting he occupied himself, under some of the old timbers, filling out rubbish. A fall occurred which knocked these timbers out and crushed him. On 18 November 1891 the accident reports show that nineteen-year-old collier John Young was killed underground by a fall of coal and clod. Prince of Wales Colliery was abandoned in 1922.

Quarry Pit, Abercarn, Ebbw Fawr Valley, Monmouthshire

Quarry Pit was opened in 1880 by the Abercarn Coal Co. On 24 June 1884 the accident reports show that twenty-three-year-old collier Henry Garland was killed underground when he and six miners were coming out together in an empty dram. They noticed the top working (moving) over them and they all got out and escaped except Henry Garland, who was in the bottom of the dram; he was caught by a stone and killed. Quarry Pit was closed in 1921.

Resolven Colliery, Glyn Neath, Vale of Neath, Glamorganshire

Resolven Colliery was opened by Cory, Yeo and Co. in 1870. On 16 October 1872 the accident reports show that thirty-five-year-old collier D. Price was killed underground by a fall of stone; on 9 February 1876 the accident reports show that haulier U. Davies was killed underground by a journey of drams and in November 1876 the accident reports show that sixty-three-year-old haulier Thomas Llewellyn was killed underground by a fall of roof. Resolven Colliery was abandoned in June 1894.

Rhas Las Pit, Dowlais, Merthyr Tydfil, Taff Vale, Glamorganshire

Rhas Las Pit was opened by Dowlais Iron Co. in 1849. On 1 October 1852 the accident reports show that twenty-nine-year-old collier John Davis was killed in the pit shaft when a guide chain broke. Rhas Las Pit was abandoned in 1922.

Rhondda Merthyr Colliery, Treherbert, Rhondda Valley, Glamorganshire

Rhondda Merthyr Colliery was opened by Rhondda Merthyr Coal Co. in 1872. On 10 July 1872 the accident reports show that thirteen-year-old collier T. Pugh was killed underground by a journey of drams; on 25 June 1875 the accident reports show that fifty-year-old J. Davies was killed when he fell down the shaft; on 7 August 1884 forty-year-old collier H. Sirle was killed underground by a fall of coal; on 16 October 1884 the accident reports show that thirty-one-year-old collier J. Rees was killed underground by a fall of roof and on 17 July 1888 the accident reports show that eighteen-year-old haulier T. Williams was killed when he fell out of the pit cage. Rhondda Merthyr Colliery was closed in 1912.

Rhymney Merthyr Colliery, Pontlottyn, Rhymney Valley, Glamorganshire

Rhymney Merthyr Colliery was sunk in 1852 by Rhymney Iron Co. On 26 April 1873 the accident reports show that fifty-two-year-old haulier Lewis Phillips was seriously injured underground by an explosion of firedamp; he died from his injuries on 14 July 1873. This was an ill-managed affair and to some extent a blameable one; on 2 June 1873 the accident reports show that twenty-five-year-old collier Richard Fernald was killed underground by a fall of coal and on 20 April 1875 the accident reports show that forty-eight-year-old collier John Jones was killed underground by a fall of roof. Rhymney Merthyr Colliery was abandoned in 1967.

Rock Colliery, Blackwood, Sirhowy Valley, Monmouthshire

Rock Colliery was sunk in 1880 by Budds of Newport. On 5 August 1860 the accident reports show that thirteen-year-old haulier Edwin Richards was killed underground when he fell under a journey of drams on the main roadway and on 16 June 1886 the accident reports show that thirty-three-year-old roadman Elijah Lewis was killed underground when he was run over by a journey of drams. He had been clearing some rubbish on the road and intended to run down in front of the drams, but they got uncoupled from the rope and overtook him. Rock Colliery was closed on Friday 14 June 1957 by the NCB.

South Wales Colliery, Abertillery, Tillery Valley, Monmouthshire

South Wales Colliery, also known as Cwmtillery Colliery, was sunk by John Russell in 1850. Shafts No.2 and No.3 date from 1850; shaft No.1 was sunk in 1858. In 1864 the mine was acquired by the South Wales Colliery Co. On 29 July 1868 the accident reports show that thirty-four-year-old roadman Richard Jones and twenty-one-year-old haulier Jonathan Williams were killed underground when they were employed to get down some top in a squeezed old road and unfortunately they placed a dram on each side of them, so that in a case of danger there was no escape whatsoever because of the narrowness of the roadway, then came the fall of roof. If there had been only one dram they could have escaped easily; on 26 March 1874 the accident reports show that twenty-eight-year-old collier Joshua Powell was killed underground by a fall of roof; on 26 January 1884 the accident reports show that fifty-five-year-old labourer John Weaver was killed when he fell sixty yards down a pit. He went from the No.1 Pit to the No.2 Pit through an engine-house with a view of getting up earlier and was seen sitting at the edge of the pit waiting, but it is not known what caused him to fall down the pit. Since this the doors leading to No.2 Pit were kept locked; on 11 March

1884 the accident reports show that seventeen-year-old collier John Warfield was seriously injured underground when he and another boy were larking with a horse, which kicked the deceased in the stomach; he died from the injuries two days later on the 13 March 1884; on 7 June 1886 the accident reports show that sixteen-year-old labourer William Townsend was killed when he fell out of the pit cage. He and seven other miners were going down the pit in the morning; six got off at the Three-Quarter landing 40 yards from the bottom and he and the other were going down, before the cage started again he turned around, his foot slipped and he fell, the space through which he fell was approximately 10½ins wide; on 6 January 1888 the accident reports show that forty-six-year-old coke burner John Milton was killed on the colliery surface when he was run over by a railway truck which he was letting down from one of the railway sidings to its loading place; on 17 July 1888 the accident reports show that fourteen-year-old collier's boy John Evans was killed underground by a fall of coal from the face where the sprags had been knocked out. He appeared to have gone in there behind his stepfather's back, with whom he was working; on 10 October 1890 the accident reports show that sixty-four-year-old collier Joseph Houlder was killed underground by a fall of roof on the engine plane as he was on his way to his working place. The road had existed and been in use for many years and it did not appear to have shown any signs of being bad at this place before the accident. It pointed to the necessity of an increased use of timber; on 28 April 1891 the accident reports show that twenty-five-year-old repairer Charles Isles was killed underground by a fall of roof. He was engaged assisting a timberman in enlarging a heading which was crushed and while his comrade was preparing timber for setting he occupied himself, under some of the old timbers, filling out rubbish. A fall occurred which knocked these timbers out and crushed him; on 25 April 1892 the accident reports show that fifty-two-year-old collier Joseph Eddy was killed underground by a scale (a normally thin friable band of stone above or below a coal seam) of about 3ins thick which suddenly burst, from the rock roof, upon him, while he was working at the face: as this was a rock roof, it was other wise very strong, but occasionally this did occur: more timber was desirable in the working places; on 15 October 1892 thirteen-year-old doorboy Abednego Aaron was killed underground when he was crushed between the side of a roadway and a dram drawn by a horse. He was travelling with the haulier instead of being stationed at the door which he had to attend to. This was a very undesirable practice, as the hauliers made the boys do a great deal of their own work. The Coroner's jury condemned the practice and the manager promised to have it stopped. On 22 November 1892 the accident reports show that eighteen-year-old collier John Evans was killed underground by a fall of coal and stone from the face of his working place in the Old Coal coal seam. He was knocking out sprags from some coal. South Wales Colliery (Cwmtillery Colliery) was closed in 1982 by the NCB.

Standard Colliery, Ynyshir, Rhondda Valley, Glamorganshire

The Standard Colliery was sunk by James 'Siamps' Thomas in 1876 and by 1878 was producing 188,366 tons of coal per year. James 'Siamps' Thomas was born in Bedwellty in 1817 and he became an underground doorboy at the age of six; he also became a fireman, an overman and a colliery manager. The Rhondda No.2 coal seam was worked extensively and the section of coal was 2ft 6ins to 3ft. Siamps built Bryn Awel, situated opposite the colliery. It is now a nursing home for the elderly. In 1884 the colliery was owned by the Ynyshir Steam Coal

Co. On 7 October 1884 the accident reports show that twenty-one-year-old collier George Price was killed underground by a fall of stone; on 23 February 1888 the accident reports show that twenty-two-year-old collier David Morgan was killed underground by a fall of roof (coal) between the gob (the waste area left behind the advancing coalface – sometimes packs are erected but usually gobs are unsupported to collapse behind the current line of supports. If coal was left behind in the gob there would be a possibility of a gob fire later) and the face of coal in the Four-Feet coal seam, which the face was propped. Two props discharged; on 2 March 1889 the accident reports show that thirty-nine-year-old mason William Cross was killed underground when he was run over by a runaway journey of drams on an engine plane while he was returning from his place of work. A shackle pin had come out and the barhook (in the event of a journey rope breaking on a slope, the barhook attached behind the last dram, digs into the floor and throws the runaway journey off the rails and prevents a potential disaster) having been neglected by the rider, 11 drams ran back a distance of 350 yards; on 18 January 1890 the accident reports show that fifty-nine-year-old labourer Richard Edwards was killed underground when he was run over by a journey on an engine drift while he was coming out from his work place; on 9 March 1891 the accident reports show that twenty-six-year-old haulier Evan Williams was found dead underground under a loaded dram which he was bringing out on a level road, 7ft high with 3ft of side space. He was supposed to have fallen off the shafts. At 10.00 a.m. on 23 March 1892 the accident reports show that sixteen-year-old collier Evan Thomas was killed underground by a fall of roof on a double parting breaking through a stage left by night repairers; at 10.00 p.m. on 13 April 1892 the accident reports show that fifty-year-old wagon trimmer Samuel Williams was killed on the colliery surface when he was crushed between a wagon and the siding wall; at 12.30 p.m. on 1 November 1892 fifty-four-year-old Christmas Jenkins, forty-seven-year-old stoker William Thomas and forty-year-old Oliver Colville were killed by an explosion of a steam boiler; at 1.00 a.m. on 19 November 1892 the accident reports show that thirty-year-old hitcher (a man at pit bottom who operates shaft signals to the banksman and winder) Frank Foxhole was killed underground when he was crushed between a dram and the side while assisting to get a dram on the rails by the aid of a haulage rope; on 31 December 1896 the accident reports show that forty-eight-year-old collier William Lloyd was killed underground by a fall of coal 3ft x 2ft x 2ft from a back slip at the coal face in the Two-Feet-Nine coal seam. He had been told to take this coal down half an hour previously; on 6 July 1899 the accident reports show that forty-year-old bratticeman (bratticeman is usually an older workman, who erects brattice [pronounced Braddish] in a district; brattice is a material for covering ventilation doors and also for directing airflow into places of workings, it was formerly made of tarred Hessian) D. Williams was killed while ascending the shaft. He was going home because he was unwell and he fell out of the cage and on 9 August 1899 the accident reports show that twenty-five-year-old haulier B. Evans was killed underground when a horse ran away, while the deceased and another haulier were riding on the front of a dram and a third man in the dram. It was the deceased's first day at the colliery.

In 1914 the Standard Collieries were amalgamated with the United National Collieries Co. Ltd who employed over 1,300 miners and produced over 36,000 tons of coal and later became part of the Ocean Coal Co. The colliery was acquired by the National Coal Board in 1947 and kept open for ventilation and pumping mine water only.

Tower Colliery, Hirwaun, Cynon Valley, Glamorganshire

The sinking of Tower No.4 Colliery began in 1941 and the pit opened in 1944.

The northern flank of the Rhigos Mountain at Hirwaun has been mined for over two centuries and the marks of early coal and iron working remain to this day.

Since the early 1800s various mines – both shafts and drifts – have operated under the name 'Tower'.

The mine centres on the No.3 Drift sunk in 1920, the 'Tower Sinkings' No.4 shaft 1941/1944 and the No.3 New Drift 1958/1959. In its early years, it belonged to the famous Crawshay family and later to Lord Merthyr. In 1935, it came under the ownership of the Powell-Duffryn Group, where it remained until nationalisation on 1 January 1947.

On 12 April 1962 at 10.30 a.m. an explosion killed nine miners and another nine were injured. Their memory will remain forever in our hearts.

In 1962, on the other side of the Rhigos, at the head of the Rhondda Fawr, Fernhill Collieries Nos 3 and 5 were planned for the link-up with Tower and in 1964 Tower and Fernhill were 'linked' underground to form a single streamlined unit, employing 860 men and produced an annual tonnage of around 250,000. Its coal at this time was semi-anthracite, used for domestic heating and for the manufacture of the popular smokeless fuel 'Phurnacite'.

In 1978 the mining programme worked an area of around four square miles and took coal from the Five-Feet and the Nine-Feet coal seams at a maximum depth of 1,500ft below the surface. The 'take' was split by a series of geological faults, running roughly NW to SE, which threw down the line of the coal seams by varying distances, up to 164ft at their worst.

Tower Colliery Pit Bottom in 1996.

Within the mining operation, there were more than ten miles of underground roadways incorporating more than seven miles of high-speed belt conveyors. All the coal was taken by conveyor through to Tower, where it was washed and blended at the nearby coal preparation plant (washery).

At the Tower end particularly, the mine is bounded by extensive old iron workings dating back several hundred years and these need to be considered very carefully when planning new developments. There were substantial reserves in the Five-Feet and Nine-Feet coal seams.

In 1978 the average maximum demand of electrical power 3293 KW, the total capital value of plant and machinery in use £202,000 and the estimated workable coal reserves was 36 million tons. The annual saleable output in 1978 was 244,021 tons, the average weekly output of saleable coal was 4,000 tons, the average output per man/shift at the coal face was 3.4 tons, the average output per man/shift overall was 1 ton, the deepest working level 1,500ft and the number of coal faces working were two. No.1 shaft depth 518ft, diameter 16ft, No.2 shaft depth, 922ft, diameter 20ft, No.3 shaft depth, 880ft, diameter elliptical 17ft 6ins x 11ft, man-winding capacity per cage wind 20, winding engines 300hp, drift length 3,000ft, coal conveying capacity per hour from pit 350 tons, average weekly washery throughput 7,500 tons, types of coal semi-anthracite, markets domestic/manufactured smokeless fuels with a fan capacity of 200,000 cubic feet per minute.

On 14 May 1986, Mardy Colliery underground link up with Tower Colliery was only half an inch out of point! Mardy No.3 and No.4 Colliery, the last colliery in the Rhondda Valley, was closed on Thursday 21 December 1990 by British Coal.

By April 1994 Tower was the last deep mine in the Cynon Valley and closure came on 23 April 1994. £2 million pounds was raised by the 239 miners who pledged £8,000 each from their redundancy payments to achieve the buy-out and successfully the Tower Employees Buy-out (TEBO) was won in October 1994 and on 23 December 1994 the ownership of Tower Colliery passed from British Coal to Goitre Tower Anthracite Limited, the new name under which TEBO would operate. On 2 January 1995 Tower miners and their families and supporters marched back to the pit to take over its ownership and flew the Red Dragon of Wales on its headgear.

Now in the third millennium and six years on, Tower's co-operative venture was producing anthracite coal from the V45 coalface in the Five-Feet coal seam. The development of the V47 coalface was also in progress. Week ending 25 March 2001 production. Face annual budget 590,551 tons, 3,993 cuts at 388 tons per cut (actual) 14,810 tons. Total (actual) saleable output to date 112,717 tons. Development advance V47 tail total 1,689 yards, V47 faceline total 233 yards. Total saleable output from development 954 tons (approximate). Tower Colliery is the last deep coal mine in South Wales and the only workers' owned colliery in the world.

The explosion at Tower Colliery on Thursday 12 April 1962 claimed the following nine miners' lives:

Names of casualties	Age	Occupation
1. E. Bond	47	labourer
2. L. Davies	37	fitter
3. T. Jones	57	collier
4. W.J. Maull	61	collier
5. D.J. Morris	51	collier
6. L.R. Price	27	collier
7. W. Smith	39	deputy
8. K. Strong	32	deputy
9. D. Williams	37	fitter

Names of Injured	Age	Occupation
1. L.W. Boulton	52	collier
2 .E. Davies	58	transfer point attendant
3. J. Jones	52	transfer point attendant
4. A. Lewis	52	ventilation official
5. A. Lewis	47	roadman
6. T. Lewis	56	transfer point attendant
7. R. Morgan	26	repairer
8. M.A. Pearce	20	apprentice electrician
9. W. Strong	55	chargeman

Extract from *The Miner* magazine of the South Wales Area National Union of Mineworkers:

In the Tower explosion, we have once again a grim reminder of the price of coal. On 12 April, when the village had hardly stirred, nine men lost their lives and an equal number were injured.

Surely we have had sufficient experience in this coal industry to avoid incidents of this kind, despite the slender margin of safety that exists. The elements of disaster are always present in a mine; gas exudes from the coal seams and can, where the ventilation circuit is deficient, accumulate in cavities and blind inclined roadways. However, we are fortunate that their presence at the same time and at the same place are rare. Modern mining has brought in its wake hazards that were little known to the pioneers in this industry. The introduction of huge machines necessitates the use of electric current as a means of power in mining operations. This calls for the exercise of great care and attention by the management in a supervisory and planning capacity and the utmost self-discipline among men and management. Safety in mines, while being a personal matter, has a big social content. The consequences of misbehaviour or error or judgment invariably have collective repercussions. Tower Colliery is producing coal today, November 2005.

Tylorstown Collieries, Tylorstown, Rhondda Valley, Glamorganshire

Sinking of Tylorstown No.8 Colliery, Cynllwyn-du South also known as Pontygwaith Colliery began in 1858. The venture failed after a short time and sinking was also twice interrupted by strikes. The working rites were then purchased by David Davis, but remained idle until 1892 when it was re-opened and sunk to the deeper coal seams. No.8 Pit ceased coaling in 1935. No.9 Colliery was opened in 1907 by David Davis and Sons Limited. The colliery was owned by the Powell Duffryn Steam Coal Co. prior to nationalisation in 1947.

Sinking of Tylorstown No.9 Colliery Cynllwyn-du North was started in 1904 and completed in 1907 by David Davis and Sons Limited.

In 1914 No.8 and No.9 Collieries supplied coal to the British Admiralty. It was of an exceptionally good quality, fit for the service and met to the fullest extent requirements of marine boilers. In 1915 No.8 Pit employed 1,989 men and No.9 Pit employed 774 men.

To give an instance of the four Ferndale Colliery groups, the group comprising Nos 8 and 9 was particularly worthy of description. No.8 Pit was first sunk by Thomas Wayne in 1858 to the Six-Feet Seam at a depth of 1,301ft 4ins and was originally called Pontygwaith Colliery and was also known locally as Cynllwyn-du Colliery. The Two-Feet-Nine and Four-Feet Seams, which lay above were won by cross-measure drivages so that the three seams might be raised from the same level.

Subsequently, No.9 Pit was opened in 1907 by David Davis and was 50 yards to the North, and this pit was carried down to the Bute coal seam at a depth of 1,525ft. Cross-measure drivages were again made to win the Yard coal seam, lying 126ft below the Bute coal seam and also to the Five-Feet coal seam lying 136ft below the Bute coal seam. Thus six coal seams had been won from this one pair of shafts. Ventilation was provided by an electrically driven fan capable of producing 300,000cu.ft of air per minute. Duplicate motors were provided for the fan each capable of producing the requisite circulation of air, so as to provide against any possible breakdown of this most essential factor in the safety of the colliery - the same safeguard being adopted at all the company's ventilating installations.

Electricity was very largely used as motive power. No.9 Pit was fitted with an electric winding engine plant, one of the first of any size used in South Wales. It was capable of raising up the shaft 1,400 tons in seven hours from a depth of 512 yards, the time taken for each wind being forty-seven seconds. All pumping and many of the underground main haulages were worked electrically. The subsidiary haulages, which were situated, further in the working were driven by blast (compressed air).

In No.8 shaft the coal was raised by the more usual steam-driven winding engine, which raised two drams of coal per wind.

A carefully designed system of watering all main haulage roads for keeping down coal dust had been in force for many years. The water was brought down from the surface by pipes. These pipes were carried along all roads, with taps placed at intervals of 40 yards; from the taps the water was sprayed over the roads. There were between thirty and forty miles of such pipes laid throughout the company's mines. As a further safeguard against the danger of coal dust explosions a stone dust plant had been laid down. In this plant suitable shale was ground to the fineness of flour, and this fine dust was taken underground and distributed over the underground roadways in such a way that it mixed with the dangerous coal dust, which was thereby rendered non-flammable.

The long-wall system had been adopted for working the seams, some of the thinner seams being cut by machines. The use of machines for the getting of coal would increase in the future, as the thicker coal seams were being depleted, necessitating the working of the thin coals.
Large drams, each carrying 30 to 32 cwts (hundred-weights), were used for bringing the coal to the surface, and these were brought from the faces to the main haulages by powerful horses and small compressed-air engines.

The progressive policy of the company was again demonstrated in the early 1900s, when all the collieries were practically re-powered. This was carried out by the putting down of a large power station. Three Sulzer cross-compound horizontal engines, each capable of 2,500bhp and coupled to 1,600 KW electric generators were first installed, then five years later a 5,000 KW turbo-generator was added to the station. The necessary steam was provided by water-tuber boilers fitted with mechanical stokers.

The main power station was a well-constituted building. It was of brick, constructed on a steel frame, which sustained the whole weight of the roof and upper floors. The interior had walls of glazed white bricks with windows on sides and roofs and was splendidly lit. A travelling crane with a lifting power of 30 tons was fitted overhead to cover the length of the building.

The average amount of electrical current distributed to the collieries was 13,000,000 BT units per annum. This power was distributed by means of overhead lines at 6,600 volts to the several pits, where in sub-stations it was reduced to suitable voltage for the various motors working pumps, fans, surface and underground haulages, etc. By the introduction of this power into the collieries, it was possible to dispense with much steam plant, boilers, etc. and thereby make a very large saving on the quantity of coal consumed at the Collieries. Tylorstown No.8 and No.9 Colliery was closed on Friday 15 October 1960 by the NCB.

Tylorstown No.6 Colliery
Pendyrus North

In 1872 the mineral rights of Pendyrus lands were bought by Alfred Tylor, after whom Tylorstown was named, and in 1873, the sinking of No.6 and No.7 shafts began. Great difficulties were encountered and it was not until 1876 that the steam coal seams were won. Coal was first despatched to Cardiff in January 1877 and subsequently, under the direction of Herbert Kirkhouse, the development of the Pendyrus Colliery was extremely rapid, output mounting from 3,252 tons in 1877 to 241,061 tons in 1893. In 1914 No.6 and No.7 Collieries also supplied coal to the British Admiralty. It was of an exceptionally good quality, fit for the service and met to the fullest extent requirements of marine boilers.

On 14 February 1884 the accident reports show that eighteen-year-old rider Frederick Teague was killed underground when he fell under a journey of drams and on 6 July November 1884 the accident reports show that twenty-eight-year-old collier David Morris and seventeen-year-old collier David Evans were killed underground by a fall of roof.

Tylorstown No.6 and No.7 Colliery Memorial in 1998. The memorial for Tylorstown No.6 and No.7 colliery was began in January 1998 by the Mid Fach River Care Group. The opening ceremony took place on May Day, 1998 and was unveiled by Dr E.I. Gwynne.

The explosion which occurred at Tylorstown Colliery on 27 January 1896 causing the deaths of fifty-seven men and boys and eighty pit ponies brought to an end the brief respite from the accidents which had become so prevalent in the South Wales Coalfields during the late nineteenth century. Then came the silence, despair and heartache in the early morning rain. Rumours spread like wildfire throughout the valley communities that a terrible disaster had occurred at Tylorstown. Wild claims were made which put the numbers of men trapped or buried as high as 700 and this naturally caused great panic among the relatives of the miners. One early newspaper report did little to calm the fears of the close-knit community.

Although the explosion occurred in No.8 Pit the worst consequences were experienced at No.7 Pit. The force of the explosion brought down heavy falls of roof and sides and cut off all expectation of life and made recovery of the casualties a very time consuming operation.

The explosion at Tylorstown Colliery on Monday 27 January 1896 claimed the following fifty-seven men and boys' lives:

Names of casualties	Age	Occupation	Names of casualties	Age	Occupation
1. Walter Barrett	17	collier	12. James Edwards	35	collier
2. John Bowen	50	fireman	13. James Evans	38	ostler
3. Abraham Charles	29	collier	14. Jesse Evans	52	fireman
4. John Collins	27	master haulier	15. Richard Evans	48	fireman
5. David Davies	26	master haulier	16. Richard D. Evans	28	fireman
6. David Davies	18	collier	17. George Gardener	25	ostler
7. Henry Davies	25	labourer	18. George Groves	47	miner
8. Richard Davies	34	collier	19. Thomas Hall	17	labourer
9. Sidney Davies	37	haulier	20. David Harris	49	collier
10. Solomon Davies	25	collier	21. Henry Harris	19	collier
11. Thomas Davies	18	collier	22. Alfred Jackson	15	collier
23. James Jackson	25	collier	41. Amos Pritchard	46	collier
24. Griffith Jenkins	35	haulier	42. Daniel Reardon	24	labourer
25. William R. Jenkins	39	collier	43. David Rosser	41	fitter
26. David Jones	27	collier	44. John Rowlands	21	collier
27. David Jones	22	collier	45. Robert Saunders	30	ostler
28. George Jones	19	labourer	46. Thomas Scourfield	32	collier
29. Gwilym Jones	29	collier	47. George Stapleton	54	ostler
30. Jacob Elias Jones	18	collier	48. James Sutton	38	ostler
31. David Lewis	22	collier	49. John Thomas	37	collier
32. George Lewis	50	labourer	50. Richard Thomas	35	collier
33. John Lewis	39	fireman	51. John Watkins	33	collier
34. Evan Morgan	34	collier	52. David Williams	22	haulier
35. Samuel Morgan	21	haulier	53. Edwin Williams	20	labourer
36. Charles Norman	22	labourer	54. Joseph Williams	20	rider
37. Albert Olding	20	collier	55. Lewis Williams	19	collier
38. John Pearce	64	miner	56. Samuel Williams	32	collier
39. Benjamin Phillips	52	fireman	57. Henry Wiltshire	17	collier
40. Isaac Pride	19	labourer			

Names of injured	Age	Occupation
1. Arthur Brodie	28	engine driver
2. Griffith Philips	?	?
3. Eddy Williams	18	engine driver

The verdict delivered from the sixteen-man jury at the Coroners' court, held at the Queens Hotel, Tylorstown, said:

We are of the opinion that the cause of the explosion was the firing of a shot in gas, in the Daniel Williams Heading at No.8 Pit. That the air passing through the faces was charged with gas and the shot came in contact with the film of gas in Daniel Williams Road and that the explosion was also accelerated by coal dust. We also are of the opinion that no one now living is responsible for the explosion.

Extract from Memorandum of Agreement for Injury by Accident:

The matter of the Workmen's Compensation Act between James John Down, 8 Hendrefadog Street, Tylorstown in the County of Glamorganshire and D. Davis & Sons of Ystrad Mynach, Hengoed in the said County, Colliery Proprietors. Be it remembered that on the 8th day of April 1913, personal injury was caused at Tylorstown No.6 Colliery, and agrees to accept the sum of £100 in full satisfaction, redemption and discharge of all claims, past, present and future for compensation competent to the said workman under the above mentioned Act arising out of the said accident or otherwise howsoever arising. He was employed as a collier and his average weekly earning computed in accordance with the above mentioned Act were £1 13s 0d. He was injured by a dram of coal going over his left leg. His nature of his injury was as follows: Fractured left tibia and fibula. He was totally incapacitated from the date of the accident up to 7th April 1914. Full compensation, various amounts. £116 16s 4d, partial compensation, various rates, £152 14s 4d. Total paid £249 10s 8d.

In 1915 Tylorstown No.6 Pit employed 617 men and the No.7 Pit employed 1,024 men. Coaling ceased in 1936 and was retained for pumping and ventilation and was finally closed with Tylorstown No.8 and No.9 Colliery on Friday 15 October 1960 by the NCB.

Tynewydd Colliery, Porth, Rhondda Valley, Glamorganshire

Tynewydd Colliery was sunk in 1852 at a depth of 270ft by the Troedyrhiw Coal Co. At approximately 4.00 p.m. on Wednesday 11 April 1877 the Tynewydd Colliery was inundated with water from the old workings of the adjoining Hinde's Upper Cymmer Colliery. At the time of the inundation there were fourteen men in the pit, of whom four were unfortunately drowned and one killed by compressed air, leaving nine men imprisoned by the water; of this number four were released after eighteen hours' imprisonment and five after nine days' imprisonment. It was in effecting the release of these latter five that those distinguished services were rendered which the conferring of the 'Albert Medal of the First Class' is intended to recognise.

The inundation of water at Tynewydd Colliery on Wednesday 11 April 1877 claimed the following five lives:

Names of casualties	Age	Occupation
1. John Hughes	50	collier
2. William Hughes	17	collier
3. William Morgan	28	collier
4. Robert Rogers	13	collier's boy
5. Edward Williams	35	collier

Until the Tynewydd Colliery disaster the Albert Medal First and Second Class had been given only for bravery in saving life at sea. Then came Queen Victoria's announcement:

The Albert Medal, hitherto only bestowed for gallantry in saving life at sea, shall be extended to similar actions on land and that the first medals struck for this purpose shall be conferred on the heroic rescuers of the Welsh Miners.

The *London Gazette* published the list on 7 August 1877 as follows:

The Queen has been graciously pleased to confer the 'Albert Medal of the First Class' on:
Daniel Thomas, Colliery Proprietor, Brithweunydd, Rhondda Valley, South Wales
William Beith, Mechanical Engineer of Harris Navigation Colliery, Quakers Yard, South Wales
Isaac Pride, Collier, Llwyncelyn Colliery, Rhondda Valley, South Wales
John William Howell, Collier, Ynyshir Colliery, Rhondda Valley, South Wales.

The following is an account of the services in respect of which the decoration has been conferred: On the 11th April 1877 the Tynewydd Colliery situated near Porth in the Rhondda Valley, South Wales was inundated with water from the old workings of the adjoining Cymmer Colliery. At the time of the inundation there were fourteen men in the pit, of whom four were unfortunately drowned and one killed by compressed air, leaving nine men imprisoned by the water; of this number four were released after eighteen hours imprisonment and five after nine days imprisonment. It was in effecting the release of these latter five that those distinguished services were rendered which the conferring of the 'Albert Medal of the First Class' is intended to recognise.

The rescuing operations consisted in driving through the barrier of coal thirty-eight yards in length, which intervened between the imprisoned men and the rescuers and kept back a large quantity of water and compressed air, this task was commenced on Monday the 16th April and was carried on until Thursday the 19th April without any great amount of danger being incurred by the rescuers, but about 1:00 p.m. on that day, when only a few yards of barrier remained, the danger from an eruption of water; the evil and immoral enemy, gas and compressed air was so great as to cause the colliers to falter. It was at this juncture that the above-mentioned four men volunteered to resume the rescuing operations, the danger of which had been greatly increased by an outburst of inflammable gas under great pressure and in such quantities as to extinguish the Davy lamps, which were being used. The danger from gas continued at intervals until 3:30 a.m. on the following morning and from that time the above four men at great peril to their own lives continued the rescuing operations until 3:00 p.m. when the five imprisoned men were safely released.

The Queen has been graciously pleased to confer the "Albert Medal of the Second Class" on:
George Albert, Collier, Tynewydd Colliery, Rhondda Valley, South Wales
Charles Baynham, Collier, Brithwynydd Colliery, Rhondda Valley, South Wales
Richard Hopkins, Collier, Ynyshir Colliery, Rhondda Valley, South Wales

Richard Howells, Overman, Tynewydd Colliery, Rhondda Valley, South Wales

Charles Oatridge, Collier, Tynewydd Colliery, Rhondda Valley, South Wales

John Williams, Collier, Pontypridd Colliery, Rhondda Valley, South Wales

Edward David, Collier, Hafod Colliery, Rhondda Valley, South Wales

William Morgan, Hafod Colliery, Rhondda Valley, South Wales

David Rees, Fireman, Tynewydd Colliery, Rhondda Valley, South Wales

Rees Thomas, Collier, Tynewydd Colliery, Rhondda Valley, South Wales.

During the five days from the 16th April to the 20th April the above eleven men were at various times engaged in cutting through the barrier of coal separating them from the five imprisoned men and while exposing their own lives to the great danger which would have resulted from an outburst of compressed air and water and to the danger which actually existed from the presence of large quantities of inflammable gas, continued to perform their work until the five men were safely rescued.

The Queen has been graciously pleased to confer the 'Albert Medal of the Second Class' on:

David Davies, Colliery Owner, Penrhiwfer, Rhondda Valley, South Wales

Thomas Jones, Colliery Owner, Ynyshir, Rhondda Valley, South Wales

Edmund Thomas, Colliery Owner, Llwyncelyn, Rhondda Valley, South Wales

James Thomas, Colliery Owner and Manager, Tynewydd, Rhondda Valley, South Wales. The part owner and Manager was in the extraordinary position of being put up for an Albert Medal for bravery and being tried for manslaughter in connection with the same affair. However, the error was noted and his name removed from the list.

Thomas Thomas, Colliery Manager, Ynyshir, Rhondda Valley, South Wales

Thomas Gedrych Davies, Colliery Manager, Tylacoch, Rhondda Valley, South Wales

David Evans, Colliery Manager, Ferndale, Rhondda Valley, South Wales

David Jones, Colliery Manager, Cymmer Level, Rhondda Valley, South Wales

Henry Lewis, Colliery Manager, Energlyn Colliery, Monmouthshire

Isaiah Thomas, Colliery Manager Brithweunydd Colliery, Rhondda Valley, South Wales

William Thomas, Colliery Manager Resolven, Near Neath, Glamorganshire.

The following is an account of the services in respect of which the decoration has been conferred:

From Thursday the 12th April when the operations for the rescue were commenced until Friday the 20th April, when the intervening barrier of coal had been cut through and the imprisoned men released, the above-named eleven men were present at different times and while being of valuable service in the rescue, exposed their own lives to the great danger which would have attended an outburst of water and compressed air, or an explosion of the inflammable gas which at different times during the rescue escaped under great pressure and in dangerous quantities. The rescuing operations consisted in driving through the barrier of coal thirty-eight yards in length, which intervened between the imprisoned men and the rescuers and kept back a large quantity of water and compressed air; this task was commenced on Monday the 16th April 1877 and was carried on until Thursday the 19th April 1877.

At 1.00 p.m. on 14 March 1895 the accident reports show that twenty-year-old collier Thomas Board on this day was acting as a hitcher, was killed underground when he attempted to jump on the rope in front of a full journey, which was coming up a drift; his foot slipped and he fell under the journey of drams. Tynewydd Colliery was closed in 1901.

Universal Colliery, Senghenydd, Aber Valley, Glamorganshire

Universal Colliery was sunk by the Universal Steam Coal Co. in 1891. The two shafts' depth was 1,950ft. Coal seams worked were the Two-Feet-Nine, Four-Feet, Six-Feet and Nine-Feet. In 1905 the Lewis Merthyr Consolidated Collieries Limited acquired the Universal Colliery, which was later to suffer the worst ever-mining disaster in British history.

The first of two appalling explosions struck at 5.10 a.m. on 24 May 1901 when eighty-two men and boys were killed in the east side of the mine about 700 yards from pit bottom. The explosion damaged both shafts and jammed the cage at pit bottom so securely in the shaft that much time had to be spent disconnecting its rope at the winding engine-house. When this was completed it was found that the other cage could not be moved down to pit bottom because of a large mass of debris in the shaft. It took five hours to clear the debris. Although the ventilation was very good, the heavy and extensive falls of roof greatly hampered rescue efforts. At pit bottom haulier William Harris was found unconscious beside the body of his dead horse. He was the only one to be brought up alive. The following quotation was taken from a memorial card that was printed for the funeral: 'Boast not thyself of tomorrow; for thou knowest not what a day will bring forth'.

The explosion at Universal Colliery on Friday 24 May 1901 claimed the following lives:

Names of casualties	Age	Occupation	Names of casualties	Age	Occupation
1. William Anslow	42	Repairer	21. George Filer	72	waller
2. Edward Bennett	39	assistant repairer	22. Thomas Fisher	49	waller
			23. Joseph Fullalove	17	repairer
3. Albert Blackmore	33	waller	24. Thomas Fullalove	47	assistant repairer
4. David Bowles	31	rider			
5. Thomas Coombs	29	assistant timberman	25. Benjamin D. Griffiths	33	haulier
			26. David Griffiths	52	assistant repairer
6. Charles H. Crocket	28	assistant repairer	27. George Griffiths	59	ostler
7. William Crook	42	repairer	28. George Griffiths	25	repairer
8. David Davies	19	timberman	29. John Harvey	19	labourer
9. Ebenezer Davies	45	fireman	30. Lewis C. Hurley	41	waller
10. John Davies	25	ripper	31. David James	43	fireman
11. John A. Davies	25	assistant repairer	32. James James	29	haulier
			33. David Jenkins	29	repairer
12. Jonah Davies	59	ostler	34. Evan John Jenkins	19	assistant repairer
13. William Davies	36	repairer			
14. William H. Davies	36	fireman	35. William John	21	assistant repairer
15. Andrew Diegan	22	waller			
16. Thomas Dobson	26	labourer	36. David Jones	26	assistant repairer
17. James Edwards	30	assistant repairer			
			37. Gwilym Jones	37	fireman
18. George Evans	31	assistant repairer	38. Henry Jones	26	repairer
			39. John Jones	32	repairer
19. John T. Evans	45	fireman	40. Robert Jones	36	waller
20. William T. Evans	33	haulier	41. Thomas Jones	61	repairer

Names of casualties	Age	Occupation	Names of casualties	Age	Occupation
42. Thomas Jones	35	ostler	62. John Pugh	27	waller
43. William C. Jones	30	ripper	63. Robert Rowlands	25	haulier
44. William Jenkin Jones	23	heading man	64. Robert W. Rowlands	58	repairer
45. Henry Layman	36	repairer	65. William D. Rowlands	24	repairer
46. Albert Edward Lee	28	haulier	66. William Sheill	49	ostler
47. Albert Lewis	19	waller	67. David Skym	17	haulier
48. Jacob Lewis	46	waller	68. Thomas Thirlfall	57	repairer
49. William J. Lewis	39	waller	69. John Thomas	43	waller
50. Llewellyn Llewellyn	49	haulier	70. John Thomas	34	repairer
51. George Lower	26	waller	71. John Thomas	31	heading man
52. Phillip Lower	18	haulier	72. Rees Thomas	39	repairer
53. Christopher Martin	31	fireman	73. William Thomas	51	repairer
54. David Morgan	46	waller	74. William Trotman	32	repairer
55. Gwilym Morgan	32	haulier	75. David Vaughan	39	repairer
56. Thomas Morgan	35	repairer	76. John Walters	26	haulier
57. William D. Morgan	20	waller	77. George Warren	61	repairer
58. Francis Muller	41	repairer	78. George Whitfield	51	haulier
59. William Parker	23	waller	79. Evan Williams	33	repairer
60. William Parry	39	heading man	80. Thomas Williams	52	repairer
61. John Phelps	26	haulier	81. William L. Williams	49	repairer

The second explosion occurred at Universal Colliery on Tuesday 14 October 1913, the worst mining disaster in the history of the British Coalfield when 439 men and boys were killed (437 killed by the explosion, two rescuers killed by falls and one rescuer killed on Wednesday 15 October 1913 – a total of 420 killed through the disaster). A sad testament to tragedy on a scale unimagined in the annals of coalmining in Britain can be found etched on the tombstones in the Aber Valley village graveyards of Eglwysilan and Penyrheol. There, the chilling epitaphs bear witness to a legacy of grief that devastated a small valley community and record a dark chapter in the history of coal mining in Glamorganshire. The inscriptions read, *Bu farw yn Nanchwa Senghenydd*. (Died in the Senghenydd Explosion).

On the morning of Tuesday 14 October 1913, the day shift assembled to descend the downcast shaft of Lancaster Pit. Because of the size of the workforce, which was around 950 men and boys, it was 8.00 a.m. before work in most of the districts was in progress. Within ten minutes, disaster was to strike on a scale previously unimagined. A terrific explosion occurred, followed by a blast which boomed up the Lancaster pit, sweeping the cage before it. Within seconds, the carriage was tossed into the winding headgear, smashing the wooden platform into a mass of splintered wreckage. The blast shook the village to its foundations, and could be heard as far away as Risca. No one there could believe it had happened. Colliery manager Mr Edward Shaw rushed to investigate and was shocked by the devastation. His immediate concern was the ventilation fan. Relieved to find it undamaged he turned his attention to the removal and replacement of the broken cage at the top of the downcast shaft. Soon, villagers came rushing to the pit, summoned by the sound of the blast. After assembling a party of volunteers, Edward Shaw together with two officials and several nightshift miners began their descent. As the rescuers left the cage, voices could be heard from the Nine-Feet coal seam a further 60ft below. Moving forward the rescuers made their way down the return road (Return is a ventilation term, the area of a mine through which travels the foul air and gases from the workings and coalfaces, on the way to the upcast shaft) in the hope that they could use the west cross-cut to gain access into the Lancaster workings. All too soon their way was barred by dense stifling smoke and an alternative means of entry through the east cross-cut was sought. With grim determination they battled through the heat and smoke and at last managed to gain access to the Lancaster shaft. Beyond the point where the steel arches ceased it was all double timbering and every pair of timbers so far as could be seen was on fire up to the entrance of No.1 North. It was like looking into a furnace. Edward Shaw knew that it would take several hours to reverse the fan to enable smoke and gases to be drawn out of the workings. This inability to quickly reverse the ventilating system was to provide damning evidence against the colliery manager Edward Shaw and the owners. Edward Shaw returned to the surface to seek outside help. The rescue teams from Dinas, Aberdare, Rhymney Valley and Crumlin were soon on the scene.

By Monday 20 October fires in No.1 North were under control, but progress in the main west level continued to be hampered by fire, fumes and falls. Rescuers continued to work undaunted by the fact that more than one-and-a-half miles still remained between them and the area where their trapped comrades lay.

A little over a month after the disaster a statement was issued giving the final death toll as 439, of which 406 bodies had been recovered and thirty-three still remained unlocated within the mine. Of the number brought out, only 346 could be positively identified.

The Coal Mines Act had been passed in 1911 and it was only two years later that the worst explosion in the history of coal mining in Great Britain occurred. As late as 1910 there had been an outburst of gas which was not got under control for four days and it had been necessary to withdraw men from the pit. It was known to be amongst the more dangerous coal mines in this country. In spite of this the owners or their agent, who was also the manager, had taken no special precautions. More than that, he had not even taken the minimum precautions enjoined on all managements by the 1911 Act. The Court of Enquiry set up by the Home Secretary (but only after repeated representations from the Executive Committee of the Miners' Federation of Great Britain) was unable to fix with complete certainty the cause of the explosion. But it was able to show that the provisions of the 1911 Act had not been carried out in a number of important respects as well as in a number of lesser matters. 'The Report of the Enquiry', wrote H.S. Jevons at the time, 'bristles with evidence of infractions of the Act'. The failure to provide apparatus by which direction of the currents of air throughout the mine could be immediately reversed was probably responsible for a large number of the deaths; had this apparatus been installed, some of the miners who had been cut off by the fire that broke out after the explosion from the intake air-current could have got fresh air. Again, the coal dust had not been dealt with properly, a matter over which the chief inspector of coal mines took a most serious view at the enquiry. On the question of the danger of unprotected electrical signalling apparatus, a special circular had been sent out by the Home Office some months earlier; on this, too, the owners had taken no steps. Not only were there these serious failures to carry out the Act, but it almost seemed on certain points as though there had been no intention to carry out the Act. For example, under the Act a means of reversing the air-current should have been provided by 1 January 1913, already more than twelve months after the passing of the Act. This had not been done. Moreover, in April 1913 the manager applied for an extension of time. This led to correspondence and a visit from a Sub-Inspector for the mine. Eventually an extension of time was granted, up to 30 September, by which time the apparatus should have been installed. When the explosion occurred a fortnight later, no work had even begun for installing the apparatus. No wonder that Commissioner Redmayne referred in his report to 'disquieting laxity in the management of the mine'. On behalf of the Home Office, the divisional mines inspector for Wales prosecuted the owners and the manager of the Universal Colliery for breaches of the Act. There were four charges against the company and seventeen against the manager, of which seven were dropped. The case was tried by three of the local magistrates. They immediately acquitted the company of all charges; they dismissed several of the charges against the manager, including the charge that coal dust had not been systematically cleared, a matter on which the chief inspector took a very grave view. On the most serious charges, (1) that he had failed to provide a means of reversing the air-current, the sentence was £10 or one month's imprisonment; and (2) that he had failed to make a daily report on conditions as to coal dust, the manager was fined £5 or fourteen days. On other failures, or rather breaches of the law, he had to pay fines of £5 and £2. Altogether, there were convictions on five charges: and total fines so small that the local Labour paper headed its report 'Miners' Lives at 1s 1¼d each'.

If indignation had been roused in the coalfields by the knowledge that the appalling loss of life in this disaster could have been prevented had the law been carried out by the coalowners and their agent, it was nothing to the widespread fury that followed the announcement of this verdict and sentence. It was felt immediately that the local magistracy were exhibiting the same partiality as had been notorious in the first half of the nineteenth century. The Home Office took measures to appeal against two of the decisions of the magistrates, in which they had dismissed the charges, namely, the charge against the owners that they had not provided within the stipulated time the apparatus for reversing the air-current (by which alone perhaps 100 lives might have been saved); and the charge against the manager that he had failed to clear accumulations of coal dust (which, if done, would certainly have diminished the force of the explosion). On the utterly insufficient sentences (i.e. 1s 1¼d a life), there was, however, no appeal lodged, nor was it possible. Not only in the coalfields but throughout a large section of the population there was strong feeling that the colliery directors should have been brought to trial for manslaughter. After all, some score years earlier, when danger was apprehended from the racing carried out between two rival railway companies on the lines to Scotland, the Home Secretary had formerly intimated that, if an accident involving fatal injuries to passengers were to occur, the directors would be prosecuted for manslaughter. It was obvious that the penalties inflicted by the magistrates for breaches of mining law bore no relation to the gravity of the offences committed by mine owners and their managers; nor were they on such a scale as to be an effective deterrent.

The occurrence of the Universal Colliery disaster also raised questions of the efficacy of the Act and of the administrative machinery by which it had to be carried out. The total inspectorate had bit by bit been raised from its original dozen to thrice the number and then, following on the act of 1911, to fourscore. This small number was responsible for over 3,000 coal mines and many more metalliferous mines and quarries. Under these conditions it is clear that inspection could not possibly be as thorough as was both desirable and necessary. Much consideration was given by the Miners' Union to questions of this kind in the two years following the passing of the Act.

After weeks of deliberation, R.A.S. Redmayne, HM Chief Inspector of Mines, in his function as commissioner, concluded in part five of his report, 'The only apparent means of ignition would be sparks from the electric signalling apparatus, or from rocks brought down by a fall.'

In April 1914 the Home Office acted on the findings of the court of inquiry by bringing seventeen charges of breaches of regulations against Edward Shaw the colliery manager and four against the owners. The latter charges, also levelled at Edward Shaw, concerned the failure to record atmospheric and air-current readings, to implement air-current reversal and the use of approved safety lamps. The hearing in July found Edward Shaw guilty on three charges of failing to keep daily records of thermometer, barometer and hygrometer readings. For all three breaches he was fined £5 0s 0d with costs of £5 5s 0d. Similar charges levelled at the colliery company were dismissed. Commenting on the serious charge of failing to provide means of air-current reversal, the chairman said, 'It has been proved to our satisfaction that on the 14 October 1913 this work had not been carried out or that at all events it was not completed. There was a non-compliance with the Act.' To the astonishment of the miners, their union and the Mines

Inspectorate, he fined Edward Shaw £10 0s 0d with £5 5s 0d costs and dismissed the charge against the owners. A further serious breach of the failure to clear coal dust from mine roads also brought, much to the consternation of the Mines Inspectorate, a dismissal of charges against Shaw. Of the original seventeen charges brought against the colliery manager, nine were dismissed and the eight of which he was found guilty brought fines that totalled £24 0s 0d.

The figure quoted after the explosion was of 809 dependent relatives and 542 dependant children; 205 widows and sixty-two parents.

One of the saddest chapters in the history of the South Wales Coalfield came to a close. It was a chapter marked with the tragic loss of 440 men and boys. I cannot put into words the deep scars this tragedy has left upon the people who lived in this Welsh mining valley in the South Wales Coalfield.

The explosion at Universal Colliery on Tuesday 14 October 1913 claimed the following 439 men and boys' lives (one rescuer was killed on Wednesday 15 October 1913, bringing a total of 440 lives lost in this coal mining disaster):

Names of casualties	Age	Occupation	Address
1. Thomas Harry Abrahams	24	collier	56 Coedcae Road, Abertridwr
2. Thomas Davies Adams	19	engineman	3 Phillip Terrace, Senghenydd
3. Frederick Alderman	45	repairer	159 Commercial Street, Senghenydd
4. Charles Francis Anderson	32	hitcher	12 Woodland Terrace, Senghenydd
5. George David Anthony	17	bratticeman	60 Caerphilly Road, Senghenydd
6 William Thomas Attewell	15	haulier	14 Pontygwindy Terrace, Caerphilly
7. Charles Baker	42	collier	18 Alexandra Terrace, Senghenydd
8. Charles Baker	14	collier's boy	18 Alexandra Terrace, Senghenydd
9. Samuel Baker	31	roadman	30 Parc Terrace, Senghenydd
10. William Baish	50	haulier	24 Cenydd Terrace, Senghenydd
11. William Barnett	15	collier's boy	99 Bartlett Street, Caerphilly
12. George Bastyn	26	collier	3 Cross Street, Senghenydd
13. Robert Bateman	18	haulier	18 High Street, Senghenydd
14. William Edward Beck	43	collier	45 Springfield Terrace, Nelson
15. John Henry Benjamin	20	collier	10 Church Road, Abertridwr
16. William Bennett	33	waller	10 James Street, Llanbradach
17. Walter Berry	27	collier	19 Ilan Road, Abertridwr
18. James Bevan	32	collier	4 Station Terrace, Senghenydd
19. John Lewis Beynon	32	waller	37 Bryn Gelli Terrace, Abertridwr
20. Samuel Bird	49	collier	42 Commercial Street, Senghenydd
21. William Bishop	37	fitter	5 Cenydd Terrace, Senghenydd
22. Samuel Booth	17	collier's helper	43 Edward Terrace, Abertridwr
23. Francis Borinetti	19	collier	13 Energlyn Terrace, Penyrheol
24. Harry Boswell	49	collier	50 High Street, Senghenydd
25. Griffith Bowen	38	collier	20 Parc Terrace, Senghenydd
26. Henry John Brooks	25	ripper	159 Commercial Street, Senghenydd
27. Charles Brown	31	hauler	23 Caerphilly Road, Senghenydd
28. Edwin Francis Bullock	30	collier	14 Dolyfelin Road, Caerphilly
29. Bertie Button	37	master haulier	87 Ilan Road, Abertridwr
30. Harold Arthur Button	26	collier	87 Ilan Road, Abertridwr
31. John Frederick Carnell	47	haulier	25 Stanley Street, Senghenydd
32. John Carpenter	23	collier	52 Dolyfelin Street, Caerphilly

33. Peter Carr	45	collier	103 Commercial Street, Senghenydd
34. Dennis Carroll	29	ripper	20 Lower Francis Street, Abertridwr
35. Timothy Carroll	35	ripper	20 Lower Francis Street, Abertridwr
36. Frederick George Chant	34	roadman	35 Grove Terrace, Senghenydd
37. John Chapman	42	waller	56 High Street, Senghenydd
38. Charles Chard	30	collier	25 Saint Cenydd Terrace, Penyrheol
39. Francis Simon Clarke	44	collier	30 Woodland Terrace, Senghenydd
40. Thomas Henry Cook	16	collier	220 Nantgarw Road, Caerphilly
41. George William Coombes	22	collier	48 Caerphilly Road, Senghenydd
42. James Colley	45	collier	13 Henry Street, Bargoed
43. Thomas J. Collier	45	collier	19 Sophia Street, Cardiff
44. Harry Copeland	33	collier	22 Saint Cenydd Terrace, Penyrheol
45. Francis Pitt Cottrell	21	collier	49 Commercial Street, Senghenydd
46. Thomas James Cottrell	19	collier	159 Commercial Street, Senghenydd
47. Thomas Cronin	26	haulier	92 Bedwas Road, Caerphilly
48. Samuel Curtis	22	collier	8 Station Road, Senghenydd
49. Stanford A. Dando	27	haulier	57 Caerphilly Road, Senghenydd
50. Benjamin Arthur Davies	25	repairer	46 Commercial Street, Senghenydd
51. David John Davies	34	haulier	17 The Huts, Senghenydd
52. David John Davies	29	waller	124 Commercial Street, Senghenydd
53. Ellis W. Davies	22	waller	4 Cwm Ceffyl Road, Abertridwr
54. George Davies	19	collier's helper	4 Cwm Ceffyl Road, Abertridwr
55. George Davies	30	collier	21 Station Terrace, Senghenydd
56. Harry Davies	32	collier	28 White Street, Caerphilly
57. Henry Davies	33	collier	167 High Street, Abertridwr
58. Henry Francis Davies	25	haulier	8 Station Road, Senghenydd
59. James Davies	44	collier	54 Caerphilly Road, Senghenydd
60. James Davies	49	collier	20 Bradford Street, Caerphilly
61. Jeffrey James Davies	28	collier	31 Stanley Street, Senghenydd
62. John Davies	27	collier	21 Station Terrace, Senghenydd
63. John Robert Davies	22	collier	145 Commercial Street, Senghenydd
64. Robert James Davies	20	collier	20 Bradford Street, Caerphilly
65. Richard John Davies	20	haulier	11 Saint Cenydd Terrace, Penyrheol
66. Thomas Davies	43	pipeman	37 Graig Terrace, Senghenydd
67. Thomas John Davies	26	haulier	74 Nantgarw Road, Caerphilly
68. William Davies	43	collier's helper	42 Kingsley Place, Senghenydd
69. William Davies	28	collier	52 Commercial Street, Senghenydd
70. William Davies	43	doorboy	33 Alexandra Terrace, Senghenydd
71. William Davies	36	repairer	67 Caerphilly Road, Senghenydd
72. William Francis Davies	27	engineman	46 Commercial Street, Senghenydd
73. Albert Edgar Dean	33	collier	240 Nantgarw Road, Caerphilly
74. Thomas Deere	41	ripper	25 Stanley Street, Senghenydd
75. Herbert James Delbridge	22	waller	31 Parc Terrace, Senghenydd
76. William Dew	39	heading man	13 Railway Terrace, Tongwynlais
77. John Dillon	36	hitcher	30 Alexandra Terrace, Senghenydd
78. William Dodge	21	collier	71 Nantgarw Road, Caerphilly
79. Mathew Henry Dorey	21	waller	1 Windsor Place, Senghenydd
80. George Henry Downes	20	collier	20 Caerphilly Road, Senghenydd

81. George Henry Downes	43	haulier	20 Caerphilly Road, Senghenydd
82. Thomas Downes	19	collier	20 Caerphilly Road, Senghenydd
83. James Druhan	26	haulier	20 Cenydd Terrace, Senghenydd
84. Ernest Edwards	25	collier	16 Woodland Terrace, Senghenydd
85. Evan Edwards	50	collier	44 Commercial Street, Senghenydd
86. George Edwards	19	collier	61 Caerphilly Road, Senghenydd
87. George Edwards	48	repairer	38 High Street, Senghenydd
88. Harry Edwards	19	collier	12 Tridwr Road, Abertridwr
89. James Edwards	42	haulier	12 Tridwr Road, Abertridwr
90. James Charles Edwards	37	collier	10 Alexandra Terrace Senghenydd
91. James David Edwards	33	collier	43 Commercial Street, Senghenydd
92. Morgan Edwards	16	collier	61 Caerphilly Road, Senghenydd
93. Richard Charles Edwards	18	collier	8 Coronation Terrace, Senghenydd
94. Richard Christopher Edwards	20	collier	5 Phillips Street, Senghenydd
95. Richard John Edwards	20	collier	44 Commercial Street, Senghenydd
96. Thomas William Edwards	30	collier	61 Caerphilly Road, Senghenydd
97. Walter Edwards	20	collier	11 High Street, Senghenydd
98. William Eldridge	14	ripper	14 High Street, Senghenydd
99. Charles Emery	61	collier	7 Thomas Street, Abertridwr
100. James Etchells	34	engineman	92 Bedwas Road, Caerphilly
101. Alfred Hugh Evans	18	collier	60 High Street, Senghenydd
102. Charles Evans	38	haulier	40 Caerphilly Road, Senghenydd
103. David Evans	51	master haulier	31 Parc Terrace, Senghenydd
104. David Richard Evans	20	haulier	25 Caerphilly Road, Senghenydd
105. Evan David Evans	22	haulier	31 Parc Terrace, Senghenydd
106. Evan Evans	44	haulier	6 Grove Terrace, Senghenydd
107. George Henry Evans	24	collier	69 Caerphilly Road, Senghenydd
108. Morgan Evans	59	collier	9 Parc Terrace, Senghenydd
109. Richard Evans	25	collier	71 High Street, Senghenydd
110. Rhys John Evans	48	incline man	189 Caerphilly Road, Senghenydd
111. Robert John Evans	19	collier	67 High Street, Senghenydd
112. Robert William Evans	38	collier	26 Stanley Street, Senghenydd
113. Thomas Evans	41	collier	52 Commercial Street, Senghenydd
116. William David Evans	18	collier	26 Parc Terrace, Senghenydd
114. William Evans	49	collier	27 Grove Terrace, Senghenydd
115. William Evans	47	collier	15 Coronation Terrace, Senghenydd
117. William John Evans	22	heading man	104 High Street, Senghenydd
118. Richard Morris Fern	19	collier	44 Lower Francis Street, Abertridwr
119. Thomas Fern	20	waller	44 Lower Francis Street, Abertridwr
120. Frank Ferris	39	roadman	78 High Street, Abertridwr
121. Harry Field	32	haulier	2 Fields Park, Newbridge
122. Frederick John Ford	35	collier	13 Bridgefield Street, Abertridwr
123. George Ford	17	collier	32 High Street, Senghenydd
124. Henry William Ford	28	collier	25 Parc Terrace, Senghenydd
125. Frederick French	21	waller	2 Gelli Terrace, Senghenydd
126. Edward Gilbert	55	pipeman (fitter)	23 Coronation Terrace, Senghenydd
127. Walter Grainger	22	collier	63 Bartlett Street, Caerphilly
128. Gomer Green	26	collier	1 Grove Terrace, Senghenydd

129. Arthur Joseph Gregory	20	master haulier	7 Kingsley Place, Senghenydd
130. Albert John Griffiths	21	waller	1 Wesleyan Cottage, Senghenydd
131. David Francis Griffiths	28	collier	125 Commercial Street, Senghenydd
132. Edward Griffiths	18	collier	3 De Barri Street, Rhydyfelin
133. Llewellyn Griffiths	32	collier	11 Graig Terrace, Senghenydd
134. James Gwynn	44	collier	3 De Barri Street, Rhydyfelin
135. Albert James Hadley	59	heading man	38 Stanley Street, Senghenydd
136. Charles Hall	36	collier	1 Station Road, Senghenydd
137. Henry Hall	35	collier	100 Commercial Street, Senghenydd
138. George Robert Hallett	14	collier's helper	36 Gwilym Street, Rhydyfelin
139. George Thomas Harrison	45	haulier	19 Cenydd Terrace, Senghenydd
140. Reginald Harrison	18	engineman	19 Cenydd Terrace, Senghenydd
141. William John Harvey	28	collier	8 Alexandra Terrace, Senghenydd
142. Thomas Hearne	42	collier	3 Graig Terrace, Senghenydd
143. William Henry Hemmings	25	rider	75 High Street, Senghenydd
144. Walter Henley	27	collier	190 Caerphilly Road, Senghenydd
145. William Henley	43	collier	38 Station Terrace, Senghenydd
146. James Herring	25	collier	8 Phillips Terrace, Senghenydd
147. John Herring	60	master haulier	7 Cenydd Terrace, Senghenydd
148. George Herrits	22	collier	169 Commercial Street, Senghenydd
149. Charles Frederick Hill	37	roadman	48 Pontygwindy Road, Caerphilly
150. David Henry Hill	16	collier's boy	21 Parc Terrace, Senghenydd
151. William Hillborne	36	repairer	46 High Street, Senghenydd
152. Samuel Augustus Hoare	37	bratticeman	13 Lower Brynhyfryd Terrace, Senghenydd
153. Frank Hollister	20	collier	18 Brynhyfryd Terrace, Senghenydd
154. Joseph Hopkins	35	collier	33 High Street, Senghenydd
155. John Howlett	39	ripper	48 High Street, Senghenydd
156. David Hughes	49	haulier	84 Thomas Street, Abertridwr
157. Hugh Hughes	22	engineman	9 Stanley Street, Senghenydd
158. Humphrey Hughes	19	collier	9 Stanley Street, Senghenydd
159. John Hughes	39	collier	21 Bridgefield Street, Abertridwr
160. Ruben Thomas Hughes	21	collier	38 Stanley Street, Senghenydd
161. William Hughes	19	waller	5 Station Terrace, Senghenydd
162. William Griffith Hughes	22	collier	60 High Street, Senghenydd
163. Francis Humphreys	33	collier	17 High Street, Senghenydd
164. Idris Wyn Humphreys	31	haulier	147 Commercial Street, Senghenydd
165. John Phillip Humphreys	23	repairer's helper	72 Commercial Street, Senghenydd
166. King Samuel Humphreys	46	repairer	19 High Street, Senghenydd
167. Richard Hunt	34	waller	34 The Huts, Senghenydd
168. Brynley Hyatt	22	repairer	51 Caerphilly Road, Senghenydd
169. William Joseph Hyatt	47	collier	51 Caerphilly Road, Senghenydd
170. William Ingram	31	collier	7 Universal Huts, Senghenydd
171. David John James	34	collier	16 Grove Terrace, Senghenydd
172. Edward James	18	collier's boy	109 Thomas Street, Abertridwr
173. Evan Hopkin James	43	haulier	24 Grove Terrace, Senghenydd
174. Richard James	26	collier	33 Cenydd Terrace, Senghenydd
175. David Jenkins	17	heading man	23 Dalton Street, Cathays, Cardiff

176. Thomas Edgar Jenkins	18	collier	23 Dalton Street, Cathays, Cardiff
177. Thomas H. Jenkins	27	hitcher	12 Kingsley Place, Senghenydd
178. William Jenkins	21	collier	186 Cairn Street, Cardiff
179. Daniel John	26	collier	68 High Street, Senghenydd
180. Owain Morien John	22	collier	10 Phillips Terrace, Senghenydd
181. William John	24	rescuer	93 Thomas Street, Abertridwr
182. Benjamin Jones	34	collier	1 Station Terrace, Senghenydd
183. Charles James Jones	51	collier	1 Woodland Terrace, Senghenydd
184. Christopher Jones	25	collier	1 Parc Cottages, Senghenydd
185. David Jones	35	collier	50 King Street, Abertridwr
186. David Jones	43	collier	1 Woodland Terrace, Senghenydd
187. David Jones	44	collier	6 Cenydd Terrace, Senghenydd
188. David John Jones	33	collier	19 Station Terrace, Senghenydd
189. Drychan Jones	23	collier	4 Hendre, Abertridwr
190. Edmund Jones	41	collier	18 Station Road, Senghenydd
191. Edward Jones	50	collier	131 Commercial Street, Senghenydd
192. Evan Jones	52	collier	152 Commercial Street, Senghenydd
193. Evan Jones	53	fireman	171 Commercial Street, Senghenydd
194. Evan Price Jones	32	collier	26 Kingsley Place, Senghenydd
195. Evan William Jones	27	haulier	18 Cenydd Terrace, Senghenydd
196. Gilbert Jones	24	haulier	26 High Street, Abertridwr
197. Harry Jones	33	collier	5 Graig Terrace, Senghenydd
198. Henry Jones	33	ripper	2 School Street, Senghenydd
199. Hugh Jones	29	collier	159 Commercial Street, Senghenydd
200. Humphrey Jones	43	collier	134 Caerphilly Road, Senghenydd
201. James Jones	44	repairer	10 Saint Cenydd Terrace, Penyrheol
202. John Jones	50	fireman	183 Commercial Street, Senghenydd
203. John Jones	34	haulier	31 Cenydd Terrace, Senghenydd
204. John Henry Jones	29	collier	68 Caerphilly Road, Senghenydd
205. John Thomas Bowen Jones	34	fireman	4 Phillips Terrace, Senghenydd
206. Morgan Jones	31	collier	8 The Huts, Senghenydd
207. Reuben Jones	14	collier	19 Phillips Terrace, Senghenydd
208. Richard Henry Jones	16	haulier	Haulfryn, Brynyfryd Terrace, Energlyn, Caerphilly
209. Richard Jones	43	repairer	38 Station Terrace, Senghenydd
210. Richard Jones	36	ripper	28 High Street, Senghenydd
211. Richard Owen Jones	18	collier	134 Caerphilly Road, Senghenydd
212. Samuel Jones	21	collier	11 Graig Terrace, Senghenydd
213. Thomas Jones	36	collier	40 King Street, Abertridwr
214. Thomas Jones	21	collier	10 Saint Cenydd Terrace, Penyrheol
215. Thomas Jones	43	collier	23 Bridgefield Street, Abertridwr
216. Thomas Jones	28	collier	107 Commercial Street, Senghenydd
217. Thomas David Jones	19	collier	138 Caerphilly Road, Senghenydd
218. Thomas John Jones	19	collier	25 Bridgefield Street, Abertridwr
219. Thomas Lloyd Jones	37	collier	16 Universal Huts, Senghenydd
220. William Jones	24	collier	2 Brynhyfryd Terrace, Senghenydd
221. William Jones	36	haulier	32 Parc Terrace, Senghenydd
222. William Jones	29	shackler	1 Woodland Terrace, Senghenydd

223. William Jones	40	haulier	114 Ilan Road, Abertridwr
224. William Abel Jones	21	waller	167 Commercial Street, Senghenydd
225. William H. Jones	29	ripper	29 Cenydd Terrace, Senghenydd
226. William John Jones	21	collier	16 Grove Terrace, Senghenydd
227. William Samuel Jones	27	collier	2 Energlyn Crescent, Penyrheol
228. Henry Keirl	33	collier	77 Caerphilly Road, Senghenydd
229. John Kelly	22	collier	4 Graig Terrace, Senghenydd
230. Daniel Kenvin	44	collier	17 Graig Terrace, Senghenydd
231. John Kenvin	20	waller	17 Graig Terrace, Senghenydd
232. Richard Davies Kestell	55	engineman	79 High Street, Senghenydd
233. Thomas D. Kestell	23	fireman	79 High Street, Senghenydd
234. William G. King	25	roadman	25 Cenydd Terrace, Senghenydd
235. Thomas Kinsey	25	collier	202 Nantgarw Road, Caerphilly
236. John Richard Kirkham	19	collier	67 High Street, Senghenydd
237. Frank James Langmaid	17	collier	44 Helen Street, Roath, Cardiff
238. Sidney Alfred Lasbury	26	ripper	15 Grove Terrace, Senghenydd
239. Charles Gordon Lewis	21	collier	5 Nydfa Road, Pengam
240. Daniel Lewis	51	roadman	142 Commercial Street, Senghenydd
241. David John Lewis	24	collier	11 Bridgefield Street, Abertridwr
242. Edward Lewis	23	engineman	10 Church street, Abertridwr
243. Edward Morgan Lewis	51	collier	188 Commercial Street, Senghenydd
244. Edward Richard Lewis	50	repairer	176 Commercial Street, Senghenydd
245. Griffith Robert Lewis	21	heading man	84 High Street, Senghenydd
246. John Lewis	35	collier	17 Caerphilly Road, Senghenydd
247. Joseph Thomas Lewis	31	collier	31 High Street, Senghenydd
248. Rowland Lewis	55	ripper	11 Caerphilly Road, Senghenydd
249. Rowland Lewis	45	haulier	84 High Street, Senghenydd
250. Rowland Edward Lewis	19	master haulier	84 High Street, Senghenydd
251. Thomas Lewis	62	labourer	95 Commercial Street, Senghenydd
252. Thomas Ivor Lewis	44	waller	37 Caerphilly Road, Senghenydd
253. Edwin Samuel Llewellyn	26	collier	10 Saint Cenydd Terrace, Penyrheol
254. Joseph Arthur Lock	20	waller	11 Woodland Terrace, Senghenydd
255. Silas Lock	17	collier	43 Stanley Street, Senghenydd
256. James Lower	18	shackler	25 Coronation Terrace, Senghenydd
257. Phillip Lower	22	overman	17 Cenydd Terrace, Senghenydd
258. John Lynch	34	collier	50 Saint Cenydd Terrace, Penyrheol
259. John Maddocks	42	collier	8 Woodland Terrace, Senghenydd
260. Thomas Maddocks	16	engineman	8 Woodland Terrace, Senghenydd
261. James Maher	37	ripper	14 Commercial Street, Senghenydd
262. Samuel John Manfield	16	repairer	45 Planet Street, Adamstown, Cardiff
263. Rodney Austin Manning	40	haulier	147 Thomas Street, Abertridwr
264. Alfred Charles Martin	23	collier	4 Caerphilly Road, Senghenydd
265. Edward Mathews	61	lamp locker man	9 Station Terrace, Penyrheol
266. Richard Mathews	37	collier	12 Station Terrace, Senghenydd
267. Albert McMahon	30	collier	38 High Street, Abertridwr
268. Thomas Probert Mendus	32	collier	1 Upper Francis Street, Abertridwr
269. Thomas E. Meredith	43	collier	13 Grove Terrace, Senghenydd
270. Alfred Milton	15	collier	15 Parc Terrace, Senghenydd

271. John Mogridge	29	banksman	69 High Street, Senghenydd
272. James Moran	24	collier	22a High Street, Senghenydd
273. Benjamin Morgan	19	collier	27 Grove Terrace, Senghenydd
274. David Morgan	29	collier	66 Ilan Road, Abertridwr
275. David Lewis Morgan	35	collier	37 Bowls Terrace, Penyrheol
276. Ernest Morgan	17	collier's helper	Tŷ Melyn House, Caerphilly
277. Francis Lewis Morgan	35	collier	16 White Street, Caerphilly
278. John Morgan	25	waller	30 Stanley Street, Senghenydd
279. Josiah Morgan	25	collier	66 Ilan Road, Abertridwr
280. Henry Joseph Morgan	24	collier	93 Ilan Road, Abertridwr
281. William Morgan snr	46	collier	Tŷ Melyn House, Caerphilly
282. William Morgan jnr	20	collier	Tŷ Melyn House, Caerphilly
283. William Morgan	35	waller	14 Brynhyfryd Terrace, Senghenydd
284. William Henry Morgan	15	collier	228 Nantgarw Road, Caerphilly
285. William Henry Morgan	33	haulier	12 Woodland Terrace, Senghenydd
286. Benjamin Morris	38	waller	43 Commercial Street, Senghenydd
287. Cadwaladr William Morris	23	collier	2 Brynhyfryd Terrace, Senghenydd
288. Edwin Morris	23	collier's boy	43 High Street, Abertridwr
289. John Morris	31	collier	18 Brynhyfryd Terrace, Senghenydd
290. Meyrick Morris	30	collier	6 School House, Senghenydd
291. Thomas John Morris	19	collier	43 High Street, Abertridwr
292. Charles Moss	20	heading man	45 Commercial Street, Senghenydd
293. Ernest Edward Mulcock	21	collier	28 White Street, Caerphilly
294. John James Muldoon	17	collier	Maesyrearll, Furnace Rd., Penyrheol
295. Lewis Musty	42	collier	8 Station Road, Senghenydd
296. Richard T. Newell	23	collier	87 Ilan Road, Abertridwr
297. Charles Owen	30	ripper	5 Station Road, Senghenydd
298. George Owen	30	collier	30 Grove Terrace, Senghenydd
299. John Griffith Owen	24	haulier	58 High Street, Senghenydd
300. Albert Parish	29	doorboy	3 Cross Street, Senghenydd
301. Charles Parry	47	collier	9 Parc Terrace, Senghenydd
302. Hugh L. Parry	28	repairer's helper	110 Caerphilly Road, Senghenydd
303. Frederick Charles Parsons	22	overman	47 Long Row, Nelson
304. William Hadley Payne	34	waller	63 Coburn Road, Cathays, Cardiff
305. Albert Edward Pegler	29	haulier	12 Phillips Terrace, Senghenydd
306. Harry Penny	27	collier	22 Saint Cenydd Terrace, Penyrheol
307. Charles Peters	22	collier	12 North Luton Place, Adamstown, Cardiff
308. John Lot Peters	27	collier	48 Bartlett Street, Caerphilly
309. Ernest Petherick	16	collier	15 Grove Terrace, Senghenydd
310. Thomas Phillips	28	haulier	8 Stanley Street, Senghenydd
311. William John Phillips	20	collier	164 Commercial Street, Senghenydd
312. George Pingree	25	shackler	30 Coburn Street, Cathays, Cardiff
313. George A. Price	28	collier	137 High Street, Abertridwr
314. Harold Price	22	collier	18 Woodland Terrace, Senghenydd
315. Idris Price	18	collier	13 Clive Street, Senghenydd
316. Benjamin Joseph Priest	36	collier	40 Ilan Road, Abertridwr
317. James Victor Priest	14	collier	40 Ilan Road, Abertridwr

318. Thomas Benjamin Priest	16	collier	40 Ilan Road, Abertridwr
319. Albert Edward Pritchard	38	collier	30 Commercial Street, Senghenydd
320. Frank Pritchard	18	collier	66 Caerphilly Road, Senghenydd
321. Henry Pritchard	29	collier	66 Caerphilly Road, Senghenydd
322. William Prosser	28	engineman	52 High Street, Senghenydd
323. John Radcliffe	44	collier	34 Grove Terrace, Senghenydd
324. David James Rees	28	collier	35 Stanley Street, Senghenydd
325. Gwilym Morgan Rees	29	collier	80 High Street, Senghenydd
326. Lewis Rees	41	mason	34 Station Terrace, Senghenydd
327. Oliver Rees	19	collier	61 Stanley Street, Senghenydd
328. Richard Rees	30	hitcher	45 Dolyfelin Street, Senghenydd
329. Richard David Rees	26	collier	16 Woodland Terrace, Senghenydd
330. Thomas Henry Rees	21	engineman	29 Cenydd Terrace, Senghenydd
331. William John Rees	43	overman	132 Commercial Street, Senghenydd
332. Richard Stephen Rex	47	collier	14 Phillips Terrace, Senghenydd
333. Arthur Morgan Richards	24	collier	112 Caerphilly Road, Senghenydd
334. David Thomas Richards	37	fireman	2 Gelli Villas, Senghenydd
335. Frederick Richards	32	ripper	22 Coronation Terrace, Senghenydd
336. John Richards	34	haulier	169 Commercial Street, Senghenydd
337. Thomas John Richards	16	engineman	112 Caerphilly Road, Senghenydd
338. Griffith Roberts	20	collier	40 Stanley Street, Senghenydd
339. Griffith Roberts	20	doorboy	84 High Street, Senghenydd
340. John Roberts	31	haulier	Gwalia Cottages, Bedwas Road, Caerphilly
341. Morgan Roberts	28	collier	16 Graig Terrace, Senghenydd
342. Robert Garfield Roberts	20	engineman	Mabon Cottages, Groeswen
343. Taliesin Roberts	24	repairer's helper	50 High Street, Abertridwr
344. William Thomas Roberts	26	repairer's helper	3 Station Terrace, Senghenydd
345. John Robinson	33	pipeman	38 Graig Terrace, Senghenydd
346. William Henry Robson	25	collier	4 Minny Street, Cardiff
347. Robert Rock	49	collier	36 Gwilym Street, Rhydyfelin
348. Peter D. Ross	20	engineman	5 Coronation Terrace, Senghenydd
349. Robert Ross	31	collier	22 Coronation Terrace, Senghenydd
350. William Ross	45	waller	22 Coronation Terrace, Senghenydd
351. William John Ross	21	haulier	22 Coronation Terrace, Senghenydd
352. James John Rosser	22	collier	59 High Street, Senghenydd
353. Edward Rowlands	48	collier	52 Dolyfelin Street, Caerphilly
354. Evan Thomas Rowlands	20	collier	2 Windsor Terrace, Abertridwr
355. John Rowlands	39	collier	77 Mill Road, Caerphilly
356. Robert John Rowlands	31	collier	11 Grove Terrace, Senghenydd
357. Samuel Rowlands	28	collier	11 Grove Terrace, Senghenydd
358. William Rowlands	59	collier	51 Stanley Street, Senghenydd
359. Thomas Saunders	21	collier	28 Upper Francis Street, Abertridwr
360. John Henry Scott	26	collier	22 Graig Terrace, Senghenydd
361. James Scriven	45	roadman	19 Clive Street, Senghenydd
362. Richard Seager	27	repairer	20 Grove Terrace, Senghenydd
363. Edmund Samuel Smale	21	collier	25 Cenydd Terrace, Senghenydd
364. Edwin John Smale	44	collier	25 Cenydd Terrace, Senghenydd

365 George Smale	43	collier	1 Thomas Street, Abertridwr
366. James Smith	31	collier	7 Brynhyfryd Terrace, Senghenydd
367. George Ernest Spreadbury	32	haulier	31 Alexandra Terrace, Senghenydd
368. Thomas Edward Stanley	31	waller	52 Commercial Street, Senghenydd
369. Edwin Albert Victor Stanton	27	collier	8 King Street, Abertridwr
370. James Edward Stephens	32	collier	32 Ilan Road, Abertridwr
371. Patrick Sullivan	37	haulier	9 Station Terrace, Senghenydd
372. William Sullivan	35	haulier	52 Saint Cenydd Terrace, Penyrheol
373. Robert John Symes	21	collier	22 Graig Terrace, Senghenydd
374. Isaac James Taylor	25	engineman	37 Graig Terrace, Senghenydd
375. William John Taylor	33	collier	28 Grove Terrace, Senghenydd
376. David Thomas	51	collier	12 Alexandra Terrace, Senghenydd
377. Enoch Rees Thomas	23	collier	66 High Street, Senghenydd
378. Henry Thomas	44	collier	9 Clive Street, Senghenydd
379. Howell Thomas	38	haulier	5 Cwm Kideg Cottages, Near Cilfynydd, Pontypridd
380. Hugh Thomas	30	haulier	8 Stanley Street, Senghenydd
381. James Thomas	39	collier	14 Brynhyfryd Terrace, Senghenydd
382. John Thomas	31	waller	34 High Street, Senghenydd
383. Joseph Thomas	33	collier	214 Nantgarw Road, Caerphilly
384. Levi James Thomas	37	collier	9 Parc Terrace, Senghenydd
385. Rees Thomas	42	fireman	9 Caerphilly Road, Senghenydd
386. Rees Thomas	23	collier	15 Bowls Terrace, Penyrheol
387. Richard Thomas	29	collier	14 Ilan Road, Abertridwr
388. Thomas Thomas	28	collier	101 Ilan Road, Abertridwr
389. Thomas Thomas	47	collier	7 Woodland Terrace, Senghenydd
390. Thomas Phillip Thomas	21	collier	165 Commercial Street, Senghenydd
391. William Thomas	24	ripper	33 High Street, Senghenydd
392. William Charles Thomas	21	collier	21 Cenydd Terrace, Senghenydd
393. William Frank Thomas	28	collier	32 High Street, Senghenydd
394 Albert William Thorne	28	collier	25 Parc Terrace, Senghenydd
395. Edwin G. Thorne		collier	30 High Street, Abertridwr
396. Francis E. Tooze	40	collier	20 Cenydd Terrace, Senghenydd
397. Thomas Tucker	21	collier	52 Stanley Street, Senghenydd
398. Alfred Rees Tudor	14	waller	33 Alexandra Terrace, Senghenydd
399. Evan Twining	14	haulier	68 Commercial Street, Senghenydd
400. Ezra Twining	30	collier	20 Station Terrace, Senghenydd
401. James Twining	16	engineman	68 Commercial Street, Senghenydd
402. John Edward Twining	28	collier	68 Commercial Street, Senghenydd
403. William Ewart Uphill	15	collier's boy	1 Station Road, Senghenydd
404. Arthur Vranch	19	collier	30 Cenydd Terrace, Senghenydd
405. Ernest Vranch	21	collier	30 Cenydd Terrace, Senghenydd
406. William Frank Waddon	22	engineman	28 Graig Terrace, Senghenydd
407. Henry Walsh	40	collier	94 Thomas Street, Senghenydd
408. Frederick Walters	20	collier	224 Nantgarw Road, Caerphilly
409. William Watkins	23	collier	Gwalia Cottages, Bedwas Road, Caerphilly
410. Evan Weston	40	master haulier	21 Grove Terrace, Senghenydd

411. Gilbert Whitcombe	37	collier	1 Universal Huts, Senghenydd
412. John White	33	collier	7 Grove Terrace, Senghenydd
413. William Henry White	24	engineman	101 Caerphilly Road, Senghenydd
414. Albert Williams	23	heading man	93 Ilan Road, Abertridwr
415. Archibald Williams	19	collier	164 Commercial Street, Senghenydd
416. Arthur Henry Williams	19	haulier	25 Cenydd Terrace, Senghenydd
417. David Williams	53	labourer	19 Parc Terrace, Senghenydd
418. David Williams	24	collier	66 High Street, Abertridwr
419. Emrys Hughes Williams	20	waller	64 High Street, Senghenydd
420. Frederick Williams	43	collier	72 Caerphilly Road, Senghenydd
421. Frederick Williams	43	collier	5 White Street, Caerphilly
422. Glyndwr Williams	14	doorboy	4 Woodland Terrace, Senghenydd
423. Gwilym Williams	72	repairer	213 Caerphilly Road, Senghenydd
424. Job Williams	52	repairer	8 High Street, Abertridwr
425. John Williams	43	ripper	35 Cenydd Terrace, Senghenydd
426. John Williams	18	collier	72 Caerphilly Road, Senghenydd
427. Joseph Williams	26	repairer's helper	2 Bryncoed Terrace, Abertridwr
428. Llewellyn Williams	21	roadman	17 Bryn Gelli Terrace, Abertridwr
429. Noah Williams	50	haulier	52 Commercial Street, Senghenydd
430. Patrick Williams	28	collier	36 Saint Cenydd Terrace, Penyrheol
431. Richard Williams	43	collier	28 Stanley Street, Senghenydd
432. William Williams	24	collier	43 Stanley Street, Senghenydd
433. William Hugh Williams	39	collier	31 Coronation Terrace, Senghenydd
434. William O. Williams	22	collier	55 High Street, Senghenydd
435. John Henry Witherall	24	haulier	55 DeWinton Terrace, Llanbradach
436. Caleb Withers	56	collier	52 Stanley Street, Senghenydd
437. William Leslie Wood	17	collier	207 Caerphilly Road, Senghenydd
438. Simeon Worman	57	timber drawer	3 Windsor Place, Senghenydd
439. Joseph Wright	33	haulier	17 Phillips Terrace, Senghenydd
440. Robert Eli Yardley	34	collier	74 Nantgarw Road, Caerphilly

A sad testament to tragedy on a scale unimagined in coal mining.
Universal Colliery was closed in 1928 and the shafts were filled and capped in 1979.

Victoria Colliery, Ebbw Vale, Ebbw Fawr Valley, Monmouthshire

During the mid-1840s construction began on new Victoria No.1 Pit at Ebbw Vale, and was completed in 1846. Although comprising of only one shaft, both coal and iron ore were raised from this water balance pit. Each cage was fitted with a tank, which could be filled with water when it was at the bank (pit top). When it was necessary to raise a dram of coal to the surface it was placed in the cage at pit bottom and the tank of the topmost cage was filled until it was heavy enough to counter-balance the weight of the loaded dram at the pit bottom and raise it to bank. The water in the descending cage was let out at the pit bottom and had to be pumped back to the surface. On Monday 21 June 1848 an accident in the pit shaft claimed the lives of eleven men and boys and an investigation revealed that the cage on pit bottom had become detached.

The accident at Victoria Colliery pit shaft on Monday 21 June claimed the following eleven men and boys' lives:

Names of casualties	Age
1. Hubert Chivers	13
2. James Davis	39
3. Richard Edwards	26
4. John Harris	47
5. John Morgan	32
6. William Owen	18
7. James Phelps	29
8. Emanuel Stilman	27
9. David Thomas	29
10. Isaac Williams	23
11. Richard Williams	27

Victoria was considered to be a safe pit. But within a year of its opening an explosion occurred. Despite this, the faith that the workings were free from hazard was not diminished. Naked flames, although thought to have been the cause of the blast, continued to be used. The disregard of this early warning was to have tragic consequences. On Thursday 2 March 1871, a second explosion claimed the lives of nineteen men and boys three pit ponies and a collier's dog.

On that day, a thorough inspection of the coalface was undertaken by John Evans the overman, who gave the all clear. These findings were later confirmed by the company's mineral agent who had also been testing the workings with a naked flame. Naked flames were used to illuminate the roadways within the mine.

At approximately 4.00 p.m. a muffled roar came from deep within the workings. Fifty-year-old fireman Jonathan Price with his deputy made a descent to investigate. On their arrival at pit bottom, both men began an intensive search of the workings. Jonathan Price unfortunately took a wrong turning. The deputy took a different route and followed the roadway down which the fresh air travelled. After a considerable time, and having received no communication from pit bottom, John Evans took it upon himself to be lowered into the darkness. Moving a short distance into the main headings he stumbled across the lifeless body of the fireman. Thinking that he was unconscious, he heroically carried his colleague to pit bottom. He was almost overcome by the choking fumes of afterdamp. There he came upon survivors, about twenty in number who had miraculously escaped both the explosion and the poisonous gas.

It was to be late evening before the arrival of a mines' inspector who signalled a fresh attempt to descend the pit. Having cleared the accumulation of foul gas, the search of the workings revealed that little damage had been sustained to the fabric of the mine. The cost to human life, however, was great with four miners killed outright while the remaining fifteen appeared to have succumbed to the suffocating carbonic acid vapour.

One of the first victims to be brought to the surface was fireman Jonathan Price. After making the initial descent into the gas filled mine, he had surrendered his life in a vain attempt to rescue those in peril below. In the disaster the Jonathan Price household was to suffer a double bereavement; among the dead was also a son, eighteen-year-old collier John Price. Yet, as so often happens, the victims of violent death are sometimes the most innocent. The true horror of the disaster was shown in the deaths of two youngsters, nineteen-year-old collier Samuel Cooke who had commenced work at the pit just a few weeks earlier so that he could better support his recently widowed mother and, perhaps the most tragic of all, of twelve-year-old doorboy Joseph Harris.

The explosion at Victoria Colliery on Thursday 2 March 1871 claimed the following nineteen men and boys' lives:

Names of casualties	Age	Occupation	Names of casualties	Age	Occupation
1. Francis Adams	21	collier	11. Thomas Mitchell	39	collier
2. John Chapman	23	collier	12. David Phillips	21	collier
3. Samuel Cooke	18	collier	13. Phillip Phillips	59	collier
4. John Evans	31	collier	14. William Plummer	24	collier
5. Charles Ford	20	collier	15. John Price	18	collier
6. John Gallope	30	collier	16. Jonathan Price	50	fireman
7. Joseph Gallope	25	collier	17. James Tanner	58	collier
8. James George	24	collier	18. George Tury	18	collier
9. Joseph Harris	12	doorboy	19. George Williams	23	haulier
10. Thomas James	21	collier			

Five days later an inquest was held at which the jury decided to view each victim in turn. The inspector, Lionel Brough, giving evidence before the Coroner, reported that a blower of gas had escaped at the coalface and been ignited by a naked flame. He further added that inadequate ventilation due to abnormal atmospheric conditions further aggravated the situation. It is interesting to note that while plans had been in existence for some time to improve the ventilation system, these had never been implemented. Remarkably the jury, after returning a verdict of accidental death, failed to mention the need for better ventilation.

On 28 May 1874 the accident reports show that twenty-seven-year-old collier Joshua Rolley was killed underground when he was crushed by a journey of drams. Victoria No.1 Pit was abandoned in July 1915.

Wattstown Colliery, Wattstown, Rhondda Valley, Glamorganshire

In the late 1870s two shafts were sunk at Pont-y-Cwtch later to be known as Wattstown and the National and was situated 1,330 yards E 14 S of Pontygwaith church. In 1880 the pit was owned by the National Steam Coal Co. and Henry Lewis was the manager. The colliery was locally known as Cwtch and the National and was sunk to the Six-Feet coal seam at a depth of 454 yards. The Rhondda No.1 coal seam was also worked at a section of top coal 10ins, clod 6ins and coal 9ins. The downcast shaft was 17ft 6ins in diameter and the upcast shaft 14ft in diameter. In 1900 the colliery employed 1,118 men. The first major explosion was on Friday 18 February 1887 and was caused by shotfiring, killing thirty-nine men and boys. The second explosion occurred on Tuesday 11 July 1905 killing 119 men and boys.

Up to 22 July 1905 rapid progress at Wattstown Colliery had been made and there was only one body left in the fatal mine. A most incredible amount of work had been done. The work of exploring the mine, dangerous at all times, but a hundredfold more dangerous after a terrible and devastating explosion, had been carried out with such efficiency and expedition that even the three unfortunate victims whose remains were a mystery did not remain so for much longer. Science, indomitable pluck and splendid endurance had penetrated the dark and formidable recesses of the tragic death-trap and that which remained of those gallant men and boys, who went down into the gloom on

Tuesday morning never to return alive, is now resting beneath a layer of earth in the little cemeteries on the hillsides. The nation sympathised; kings and councils telegraphed their sympathy.

Not the least pathetic in this tear-stained drama of human struggle for existence is the fact that so many boys had lost their lives. When the history of Wattstown village comes to be written, will those boys be forgotten? Will the future historian, in chronicling the perils, the horrors which the miner of a bygone age had to face in his daily pursuit of his bread and cheese, forget the boys who died so young? Surely their memories will linger long in the annals of the coalfield; the very ferocity of their death will serve to keep their memories green for many a year to come.

Of the 119 victims, no less than seventy-five were unmarried; of those who were fourteen years of age and under there were fourteen; between fourteen and sixteen there were nineteen; between sixteen and twenty there were twenty-two; between twenty and thirty there were twenty-four; between thirty and forty there were twenty-five; between forty and fifty there were nine; between fifty and sixty there were five and between sixty and seventy there was one. Nearly half of the victims were lads under twenty years of age.

Opening of the Inquest
The inquest on the victims was opened at the Wattstown Hotel by Mr P.J. Rhys, district Coroner, and a jury of fifteen of whom Mr David Williams was elected foreman, when merely formal evidence relating to identification was taken.

Messages from the King
During Thursday 13 July 1905 in the afternoon the following message was received from Lord Knollys on behalf of the King:

> To the Manager, Wattstown Colliery, Pontypridd, Wales. The King is anxious to express to you personally, to the widows, orphans, and other relations of those who have lost their lives in the recent colliery accident, the profound sympathy which he and the Queen entertain for them on the overwhelming calamity which has befallen upon them. Their Majesties feel most sincerely and deeply for them in their great sorrow.
> Lord Knollys.

Mr F.A. Grey, Chief Inspector of Mines, received the following telegram:

> The King is deeply grieved to hear of the terrible disaster at the National Colliery. His Majesty commands me to express his heartfelt sympathy with families of those who have lost their lives.
> Akers-Douglas, Home Office.

Expression of Sympathy from the Prince and Princess of Wales
The managing director received the following message from the Prince and Princess of Wales on Saturday morning:

Marlborough House, Pall Mall, S. W.
14th July 1905
To the Managing Director, Wattstown Colliery, Pontypridd.

> Dear Sir,
> The Prince and Princess of Wales have followed with deep sorrow the heartrending details of the terrible colliery accident. Their Royal Highnesses ask me to beg you to convey to all the mourners

and bereaved ones the assurance of their true sympathy. This grievous calamity seems to come home especially to his Royal Highness after his very recent visit to the Principality.

Believe me, dear Sir, yours very faithfully, Arthur Bigge.

The Funerals

The scenes on Friday 14 July in the streets of Wattstown, Ynyshir and Porth were impressive in the extreme, as huge processions of mourning colliers passed slowly and almost silently along on their way to Llethrddu Cemetery, Trealaw, where the bodies of twelve of the victims of the disaster at the Wattstown Colliery were interred. Soon after two o'clock a great gathering began to assemble near Wattstown Bridge. The body of the late manager Mr William Meredith was due to leave his residence, Glenside, only a few hundred yards away, while at this time a hearse and several biers had brought other bodies from Tylorstown, Pontygwaith and parts of Wattstown.

When the long funeral procession was finally formed it extended for over a mile and it took twenty-eight minutes to go over the bridge. It was silently and reverently watched by many sorrowing women and wondering little children as it continued its long and painful journey to the burying-ground. At its head walked a group of ministers who were to perform the funeral rites; after these came a long line of the Wattstown Colliery Officials and representatives of other collieries in the neighbourhood, and then the hearse bearing the body of the manager, Mr William Meredith, and the coaches which carried the chief mourners. Then, again, came another long line of black-coated workmen walking four-abreast, after these another hearse, and then more vehicles, cabs, brakes, carriages and traps of all descriptions. Here and there appeared a bier with its burden borne reverently upon the shoulders of toil hardened colliers, while between them walked or rode mourners, and still more mourners.

The majority of the bodies were interred at Llethrddu Cemetery on Saturday 15th. The scenes along the route were such as will live in the memory of those who witnessed them as long as they live. From where the road turns up to the Rhondda Fawr at Porth up to Llethrddu Cemetery the roadsides were lined with people, thousands upon thousands viewing the sorrowful cortege as it made its slow progress towards the cemetery. Crowds from all parts of the Rhondda Valleys and from many distant places had come to pay their tributes to the dead. The funeral procession was four or five miles long; the first part of the procession entering through the cemetery gates at Trealaw almost before the last portion had left Wattstown. The scenes at the gravesides were very moving, especially where two or even three members of the same family were buried at the same time. Young women wept for their sweethearts and husbands; mothers for their sons and children for their fathers. In some cases the extent of the blow could be hardly realised. Relatives stood half dazed, dry eyed, looking at the shell which contained the mortal remains of their loved ones being lowered into the earth from which they sprung. Eyes could not weep those saving tears; but imprinted on many faces were furrows of grief in its most poignant form, with no warm spring of human tears to relieve the intense pain within. It was indeed a black Saturday, black for the thousands of poor people who buried all their loved ones under a few feet of cold clay. Five of the victims were buried at Treorchy where an immense throng had awaited the arrival of the bodies. One corpse was conveyed by rail, the Taff Vale Railway Co. providing a special train. The body of William Thomas John, 29 William Street, Ynyshir, was accompanied by a host of sympathetic friends and relatives. The Ynyshir Drum and Fife Band, of which the deceased was a member, was in attendance, and played the Dead March with thrilling effect. The other bodies soon followed, these also were accompanied by a sorrowful throng. Plaintive and pathetic were the sounds of the old Welsh hymns as they were sung with a sadness befitting the sorrowful occasion. They extended to the heart of every listener. Men looked hard, trying to battle against the tears that would well into their eyes; women wept copiously, tears were always the greatest relief on occasions such as this. The Workmen's Committee made excellent arrangements for the funerals. Great assistance was rendered by Messrs. D. Watts Morgan, T. James (miners' agent) and Mr. Edgar Jones, BA, Wattstown.

Sunday's Interments
Four more victims were interred on Sunday 16th. Sunday Schools were abandoned in all places of worship and there was witnessed another huge procession scarcely less in length than that of the preceding day.

Progress at the Pit
The Thursday 13th, night shift, under Mr Jacob of Ferndale and Mr Griffiths of Tylorstown, which came up on Friday morning, did not discover any bodies during the night. Each shift worked eight hours but occasionally it was found at the time advisable to continue operations even for twelve hours. It was the rule that each shift should make the places safe for the succeeding one before returning to the surface, otherwise much extra labour might be entailed and the places rendered dangerous to the rescuing parties owing to the squeezes (the increasing pressure of a weak roof in mine workings, detected by the crushing of timber supports and the bending of steel arches – sometimes accompanied by audible cracking of roof strata. Normally a slow process).

On Friday 14th all the stretchers, brattice cloths, and other materials utilised at the mortuary were burnt.

The shift that went down on Friday morning directed their attention to clearing the falls, and about noon they came across the body of Charles Perry a roadman from Alma House, Wattstown which was subsequently brought to the surface. The body of his son was recovered on Wednesday night.

A section of the afternoon shift on Friday ascended shortly after four o'clock, and reported that they had been able to penetrate to the part of the mine which had hitherto remained unexplored, the whole of the workings having now been gone through. Under a fall they discovered some articles of clothing and one of the party felt a body under the debris. Steps were then taken to clear the fall so that the body could be brought up the pit.

Another Body Recovered on Saturday 15th
While a small band of men were engaged in Reynolds' dip, they discovered under a fall the body of fourteen-year-old J.H. Davies of 28 Margaret Street, Pontygwaith The corpse was brought to bank about noon, immediately coffined, and conveyed to the parents' house.

A fy machgen bach i yw hwna? (Is that my little boy there?) sadly queried a grieving father.

Two more bodies were reported to have been discovered on the morning of Thursday 13th, those of sinker, Elias Roberts, 4 Danygraig Terrace and fourteen-year-old collier's boy David Powell, 7 Chapel Street, Wattstown. The lad Powell was found in Taylor's heading and bore every appearance of having died through suffocation, whilst Elias was found in the water in the sump and was apparently discovered more by accident than anything else. It appeared that in the work of clearing the water, the bowc (a bucket or vessel used when shaft-sinking, for the transporting of men and materials) was noticed to be going very irregular. Grappling irons were at once dropped into the water, with the result that they caught in the man's belt. The two bodies were in no way mutilated, though naturally they were considerably decomposed. It is understood that Elias was to be buried on Friday 14th at Eglwysilan and the boy David Powell at Llanwynno. There was now only one more body to be recovered, that of David Davies, the fireman, which was almost certain to be found under the big falls when they were being cleared. No man had laboured more strenuously since the explosion occurred than Dr Thomas Davies, medical officer for the colliery. Called to the scene at noon on Tuesday 11th he had not had a moment's rest up to Wednesday night. In view of the fact that only two or three men had been brought up alive Dr Davies's labours had been confined to the blacksmiths' shop, where he examined every body as it was brought in, and jotted down notes regarding its condition. 'Is the nature of the injuries sustained by the victims very serious, doctor?' asked a Pressman. 'Yes, in many cases', replied Dr Davies. 'There are numerous instances where limbs are very badly fractured and others, again, have their skulls fractured.' 'In most of these cases death probably resulted from the fractures?' 'Not necessarily. In a great many cases, even after the fractures had been sustained from the force of the explosion, death was probably due to the effects of the afterdamp.'

Saturday 29 July 1905
Matthew Davies, the sole survivor of the Wattstown explosion, was reported to be making satisfactory progress towards recovery and was able to take substantial nourishment. He still suffered considerable pain, but the inflamed condition of the burns on the hands and face showed material improvement, and he was thought to be completely out of danger.

Coroner's Inquiry and the Verdict
The Coroner carefully received the evidence, and after approximately an hour's deliberation the jury returned into court, where the foreman said they were unanimous in finding that 'in our opinion the explosion of gas was caused by shot firing in the barrier of coal at the cross-heading between the sinking pit and the upcast pit'.
The jury also recommended:

(1) That in our opinion shotfiring should be absolutely prohibited except between shifts and only shotmen should be in the pit at the time.
(2) That a thorough system of watering roadways, sides, and roof should be compulsory.
(3) That the authorities should see that the existing regulations as to the issue and use of explosives be stringently carried out.

Mr Rhys Williams said that Mr D. Watts Morgan desired to call attention to the facilities given by the company to all persons who had business at the colliery. He desired to thank the authorities for those facilities, and if he had been put in the box he would have said so himself. Mr Milner Jones also expressed admiration of all those who went down the mine after the explosion, the managers, and inspectors and others who risked their lives. The Coroner said that this was one of the characteristics of a colliery population. The difficulty was to prevent the men overfilling the cage and descending the mine after a tragedy.

The explosion at Wattstown Colliery on Tuesday 11 July claimed the lives of the following 119 men and boys:

Names of casualties	Age	Occupation	Address
1. James Baines	55	sinker	5 Wind Street, Ynyshir
2. George Basset	14	doorboy	29 Hillside Terrace, Wattstown

Names of casualties	Age	Occupation	Address
3. William G. Basset	14	doorboy	29 Hillside Terrace, Wattstown
4. Samuel Beard	14	collier's boy	34 Hillside Terrace, Wattstown
5. John Benjamin	40	collier	1 James Terrace, Ynyshir
6. Ammon Billett	22	collier	16 Madeline Street, Pontygwaith
7. Robert Billett	34	haulier	22 Furnace Road, Pontygwaith
8. Samuel Bird	16	collier's boy	9 Hillside Terrace, Wattstown
9. George Chedzie	18	labourer	12 Graig Street, Pontygwaith
10. Charles Clancey	18	collier	Anchor Terrace, Taffs Well
11. John Clancey	38	collier	Anchor Terrace, Taffs Well
12. Robert Cross	38	collier	50 William Street, Ynyshir
13. William Daniel	40	collier	7 John Street, Ynyshir
14. Charles Davies	18	haulier	4 Hillside Terrace, Wattstown
15. Charles Henry Davies	15	collier's boy	5 William Street, Ynyshir
16. Daniel G. Davies	23	haulier	23 Slope Cottages, Porth
17. David Davies	37	fireman	29 Wind Street, Ynyshir
18 David Davies	37	collier	2 Penrhys Cottages, Penrhys
19. David Godfrey Davies	26	collier	2 Lower Bailey Street, Wattstown
20. Enoch Davies	22	collier	38 Edmund Street, Tylorstown
21. Isaac Davies	29	sinker engineman	14 Dolycoed Terrace, Tylorstown
22. John Davies	26	haulier	3 Pleasant View, Wattstown
23. John H. Davies	14	collier's boy	28 Margaret Street, Pontygwaith
24. Joseph E. Davies	18	collier	38 Fairfield Terrace, Ynyshir
25. Thomas Davies	38	collier	50 Hillside Terrace, Wattstown
26. Thomas Davies	38	master haulier	4 Hillside Terrace, Wattstown
27. Thomas Davies	40	collier	50 Hillside Terrace, Wattstown
28. Thomas Davies	45	collier	9 Maindy Terrace, Ynyshir
29. William Eastment	42	collier	29 Bailey Street, Wattstown
30. Gwilym Edmunds	19	collier	Rose Cottage, Pentyrch
31. Thomas G. Edwards	23	haulier	19 Western Terrace, Ynyshir
32. George Evans	26	collier	13 New Houses, Wattstown
33. Morgan Richard Evans	26	haulier	46 South Street, Ynyshir
34. William Henry Evans	17	haulier	46 South Street, Ynyshir
35. William John Evans	17	collier	5 John Street, Ynyshir
36. William John Evans	17	collier's boy	50 Ynyshir Road, Ynyshir
37. Fred Fletcher	25	collier	73 Aberhondda Road, Porth
38. Thomas Flower	41	collier	49 Brondeg Street, Tylorstown
39. James Gibbons	45	collier	42 Margaret Street, Pontygwaith
40. John Gibbons	20	collier	42 Margaret Street, Pontygwaith
41. Thomas Gibbons	15	collier	42 Margaret Street, Pontygwaith
42. William Henry Goldsworthy	20	haulier	23 Hillside Terrace, Wattstown
43. Lewis William Hallett	16	collier	16 Graig-y-Haulfa, Treforest
44. Robert Hallett	38	collier	16 Graig-y-Haulfa, Treforest
45. James Healing	14	doorboy	32 Bailey Street, Wattstown
46. John Howells	42	collier	21 Weston Terrace, Ynyshir
47. Thomas D. Howells	15	collier's boy	21 Weston Terrace, Ynyshir
48. William Ernest Hudd	16	collier's boy	44 Hillside Terrace, Wattstown

Names of casualties	Age	Occupation	Address
49. Evan John	18	collier	2 Chapel Street, Wattstown
50. David Johnson	16	labourer	51 Hillside Terrace, Wattstown
51. David Johnson	64	collier	57 Hillside Terrace, Wattstown
52. Isaac Jones	17	collier	19 Middle Terrace, Stanleytown
53. John Jones	36	collier	42 Margaret Street, Pontygwaith
54. Thomas Jones	51	collier	7 New Houses, Taffs Well
55. Thomas Jones	16	collier	45 Hillside Terrace, Wattstown
56. William Jones	50	sinker	29 Aberllechau Road, Wattstown
57. William Jones	60	collier	29 Aberllechau Road, Wattstown
58. William Thomas John	23	collier	29 William Street, Ynyshir
59. Arthur Kemp	43	timberman	72 Pleasant View, Wattstown
60. Alfred King	22	collier	36 Bailey Street, Wattstown
61. Thomas King	47	collier	36 Bailey Street, Wattstown
62. Benjamin Lewis	53	collier	54 Madeline Street, Pontygwaith
63. Benjamin Lewis	47	collier	5 Pleasant View, Tylorstown
64. Thomas Lillicrop	25	haulier	18 School Street, Wattstown
65. William Henry Lloyd	16	collier's boy	1 Hillside Terrace, Wattstown
66. Florence Mahoney	17	collier's boy	30 Lower Bailey Street, Wattstown
67. Alfred Marshall	33	collier	22 Penylan Terrace, Taffs Well
68. Samuel Mason	34	collier	9 Hillside Terrace, Wattstown
69. Mr William Meredith	55	manager	Glenside House, Wattstown
70. Edward Morgan	16	collier	Gellidawel, Pentyrch
71. Enoch Morgan	59	haulier	35 Aberllechau Road, Wattstown
72. John Morgan	25	collier	28 Hillside Terrace, Wattstown
73. John Morgan	59	repairer	13 Phillip Terrace, Trehafod
74. William Morgan	18	haulier	17 Aberllechau Road, Wattstown
75. William Morgan	15	collier	54 Hillside Terrace, Wattstown
76. William Morgan	17	collier	35 Aberllechau Road, Wattstown
77. William John Morley	27	haulier	Porth Station Coffee Tavern, Porth
78. David Thomas Morris	15	collier's boy	15 Heol-y-Twyn, Wattstown
79. Thomas Owen	33	sinker	5 Wind Street, Ynyshir
80. Charles Perry	50	roadman	Alma House, Wattstown
81. Charles Evan Perry	19	roadman	Alma House, Wattstown
82. George Perryman	38	collier	1 James Street, Ynyshir
83. Thomas Perryman	19	collier	1 James Street, Ynyshir
84. William Perryman	14	collier's boy	1 James Street, Ynyshir
85. David Phillips	26	collier	6 Deri Terrace, Pontygwaith
86. David Powell	15	collier's boy	7 Chapel Street, Wattstown
87. Oliver Pritchard	38	collier	Gellidawel, Pentyrch
88. John H. Probert	19	collier	Old Pit Houses, Ynyshir
89. Thomas Prosser	16	collier' boy	30 Lower Bailey Street, Wattstown
90. David Rees	38	collier	19 School Street, Wattstown
91. David John Rees	50	collier	19 School Street, Wattstown
92. David John Rees	40	collier	21 South Street, Ynyshir
93. John Rees	17	collier	47 Brewery Street, Pontygwaith
94. John Rees	37	collier	47 Brewery Street, Pontygwaith
95. John Reeves	16	hitcher	62 Hillside Terrace, Wattstown

Names of casualties	Age	Occupation	Address
96. Alfred Richards	40	collier	22 Pontypridd Road, Porth
97. William G. Richards	42	fireman	20 Pontypridd Road, Porth
98. Elias Roberts	41	sinker	4 Danygraig Terrace, Ynyshir
99. Edward John Sampson	18	collier's boy	42 Hillside Terrace, Wattstown
100. Samuel Smith	14	collier's boy	6 Hillside Terrace, Wattstown
101. Thomas Henry Smith	17	labourer	13 Bryn Terrace, Wattstown
102. Morgan Stewart	15	collier's boy	1 Bryn Terrace, Wattstown
103. William Thomas	17	collier	13 Hillside Terrace, Wattstown
104. John Tingle	14	collier's boy	8 Upper Gynor Place, Ynyshir
105. John Turberville	14	collier's boy	6 Pleasant View, Wattstown
106. Albert Uzzell	40	collier	13 Pleasant View, Wattstown
107. John Uzzell	14	collier's boy	13 Pleasant View, Wattstown
108. Benjamin Walters	37	collier	20 Graig Road, Ynyshir
109. John Richard Walters	44	haulier	3 Graig Road, Ynyshir
110. David Williams	26	collier	15 Aberllechau Road, Wattstown
111. Edwin Charles Williams	16	collier's boy	11 Hillside Terrace, Wattstown
112. Idris Williams	21	collier	15 Aberllechau Road, Wattstown
113. John Williams	44	haulier	43 Margaret Street, Pontygwaith
114. John Meredith Williams	14	doorboy	11 Bailey Street, Wattstown
115. Richard Williams	17	collier	11 Hillside Terrace, Wattstown
116. Thomas Williams	16	haulier	20 Bailey Street, Wattstown
117. William Albert Williams	13	collier's boy	14 School Street, Wattstown
118. Frank Wiltshire	14	collier's boy	4 Bailey Street, Wattstown
119. R. Yell	20	haulier	19 Western Terrace, Ynyshir

This explosion was caused by shotfiring.

On 12 September 1905 the accidents reports show that twenty-five-year-old repairer G. Jones was killed underground. Wattstown Colliery was closed on Friday 22 November 1968 by the NCB.

Waunllwyd Colliery, Waunllwyd, Ebbw Fawr Valley, Monmouthshire

There was no joy in thier hearts, only sorrow and pain.

Waunllwyd Colliery was situated close to the Victoria Colliery and was sunk in 1876 by Ebbw Vale Steel Iron & Coal Co. and the shaft depth was 816ft. It was considered by those who worked there to be a safe pit. On 26 September 1879 an explosion killed three miners and sixteen pit ponies. On Sunday night which was the maintenance and preparation shift a small group of miners descended into the pit to prepare the mine for the early morning shift that would begin at 6.00 a.m. the following day. Those who generally entered the pit were the night fireman, the furnace man and the ostlers who prepared the horses for the coming day's work. The fireman carried out the safety checks, the workings were deemed safe and the men entered into the districts each contemplating upon their various duties. It was approximately 5.30 a.m. that a disturbance was felt coming from somewhere underground. On the arrival of the pit manager, he made an immediate descent into the pit to carry out an inspection. It was discovered that an explosion had occurred in the stable area of the mine. In a short space of time the rescuers came across the bodies of three miners, all of whom had been badly burned. There was no joy in their hearts only sorrow and pain. The first of the unfortunate victims to be brought to the surface was the furnace man. By midday the two remaining bodies, those of William Griffiths and his son, were recovered. Remarkably, two night overmen and a young man, who were working deeper within the workings, heard nothing of the explosion and had to be told about their narrow escape. The remains of sixteen pit ponies were also discovered in the stables. It was very fortunate that the explosion occurred so early in the morning, for waiting to enter the mine, by way of the down cast shaft, was the morning shift which comprised of 200 men and boys.

At the inquest evidence was given that the workings of the pit were well ventilated and that there had been no detectable build-up of any gas. The court was adjourned and reconvened the following Monday morning when further witnesses were called. It was found that during the fateful Sunday night a ventilating door in the mine had been left open. The pit fireman, Timothy Griffiths, discovered and immediately closed the door, restoring correct ventilation to the underground workings. However, he failed to test for gas. Had he done so, the dangerous accumulation of firedamp which had built up due to disruption of the airways would have been detected. It was thought that during the time that the door was open, gas had gathered in some deadly quantity. With the closing of the ventilation door and the resumption of the airflow, the firedamp had been driven into the stables where naked flames burned. The explosion was then an inevitable consequence.

The explosion at Waunllwyd Colliery on Sunday 26 September 1879 claimed the lives of the following three men and boys:

Names of casualties	Occupation
1. William Griffiths snr	ostler
2. William Griffiths jnr	ostler
3. John Jones	furnaceman

The findings of the Coroner were that, 'The explosion was accidentally caused by Timothy Griffiths, the fireman, closing a door in the mine, the door having been negligently left open on Saturday night by some person unknown'. And so the blame for the explosion, and ultimately the deaths of the three men, was laid firmly on the shoulders of the fireman. The Coroner believed Griffiths to be guilty of a dereliction of duty. Indeed, in his final summing up, he recommended that, 'The Ebbw Vale Company not employ Timothy Griffiths as a fireman any further'.

On 1 January 1902 the accidents reports show that twenty-six-year-old haulier Thomas John Lewis was injured when his journey caught a stick of timber lying at the side of the road, causing it to strike and fracture his leg. He died on 6 February 1902 and on 12 September 1905 the accidents reports show that forty-one-year-old repairer Rice Jones was killed underground by a fall of stone 20-30lbs in weight from the side of a road where he had just finished his food. Waunllwyd Colliery was closed on Monday 30 December 1963 by the NCB.

Yard Vein Level, Varteg, Avon Lwyd Valley, Monmouthshire

Yard Vein Level (a level is a tunnel driven horizontally or on a slight gradient to connect underground workings with the surface) was opened by J&C Bailey in 1851. On 12 November 1860 the accident reports show that forty-eight-year-old collier Thomas Self was killed underground when a foot of clod (thin layers of mudstone directly above a seam of coal, normally it falls with the coal during mining) fell on him, it had not been pulled down. Yard Vein Level was abandoned in 1887.

Ynyscedwyn Colliery, Ystradgynlais, Swansea Valley, Breconshire

Ynyscedwyn (The Sced) Colliery was sunk in 1852 and was owned by the Ynyscedwyn Iron Co. Close to the pithead were a variety of buildings associated with generating power. At the end of the eighteenth century and through much of the nineteenth century, tall beam engine-houses housing mighty pumping engines with a myriad of flimsy and variable wooden headframes attached dominated colliery sites. In the early nineteenth century the twin functions of pumping and winding were often combined. In 1967 the Ynyscedwyn manager was D.L. Evans (4,140 First Class) and the undermanager was R.P. Herrington (6,084 First Class).

On 10 August 1853 the accident reports show that eleven-year-old labourer Richard Davies was killed by railway drams passing over him and on 20 February 1891 the accident reports show that forty-four-year-old collier Dan Hopkins was injured underground when he was crushed by a runaway journey of drams on the main heading as he was returning from his place of work. He died on 2 March 1891. Ynyscedwyn Colliery was closed on Saturday 2 March 1968 by the NCB.

Ynysyfeio Colliery, Ynyswen, Rhondda Valley, Glamorganshire

Ynysyfeio Colliery. The mineral property of 1,000 acres was purchased in 1854 by the Troedyrhiw Coal Co. and was sunk by James Thomas of Ynyshir and his partners, Mathew Cope of Cardiff and John Lewis of Aberdare. On 29 June 1868 the accident reports show that fourteen-year-old doorboy J. Evans was killed underground by a journey of drams; on 15 October 1874 the accident reports show that twenty-nine-year-old collier M. Lewis was killed underground by a fall of stone; on 7 September 1875 the accident reports show that labourer J. Thomas was killed underground by an explosion of gas; on 28 September 1876 the accident reports show that twenty-one-year-old haulier T. Davies was killed underground by a journey of drams; on 5 January 1886 the accident reports show that thirty-one-year-old ripper (miners who ripped away the roof and the floor of a seam in a coal mine so that there was sufficient height to bring horses up to the coalface) John Edwards was killed underground by a fall of roof while ripping in a heading and on 11 February 1889 the accident reports show

Ynysfaio Colliery, Ynyswen, in 1910. The colliery stood at 698ft OD. The photograph was taken on top of the pit (pit bank). The mineral property of 1,000 acres was purchased in 1854 by the Troedyrhiw Coal Co. and was sunk by James Thomas of Ynyshir and his partners, Mathew Cope of Cardiff and John Lewis of Aberdare. In 1874 the colliery output was around 36,000 tons. On 29 June 1868 the accident reports show that fourteen-year-old doorboy J. Evans was killed by a journey of drams. The colliery was owned by the Powell Duffryn Steam Coal Co. prior to nationalisation. Ynysfaio Colliery was acquired by the NCB in 1947 and employed three men for pumping mine water.

that twenty-one-year-old collier Nicholas Lewis was injured underground when he was struck on his head by a small stone from the roof in the Nine-Feet coal seam with a section of coal of 3ft 8ins. The longwall system was in use (longwall [Welsh: *wal hir*] is a method of mining coal with all the colliers of that district manning one lengthy coalface, It would have been hand-got earlier and machine cut later. No pillars are left behind in a longwall face and roof allowed to cave in behind the line of supports. Some faces would need intermediate packs if roof conditions were inferior). He died from an abscess on the brain on 14 March 1889. Ynysfeio Colliery was acquired by the National Coal Board in 1947 and employed three men for pumping mine water. Ynysfeio Colliery was closed in January 1969 by the NCB.

Some Final Thoughts

Once again, a sad reminder of the true price of coal that fuelled an Empire. Mighty industries come and go but Mother Nature ultimately prevails and we are left with the memories of human toil and the close knit communities which are their legacy.

A sudden change; at God's command they fell; They had no chance to bid their friends farewell,
Swift came the blast, without a warning given, And bid them haste to meet their God in Heaven.
Yn Angof ni chant fod. (They will not be forgotten).

Prior to 1849 the explosions in coal mines were rare. At Plymouth Colliery, in 1801 the first was simply a trivial burn and from then on up to 1849 the accidents were rare. The custom used to be for the men to go into the levels on Monday morning and, taking off their coats, literally to dust the gas out. It was when levels gave way to pits and from shallow openings to deep workings, that the fire fiend began to assume full proportions and so continued up to the margin of our enquiry, rioting every now and then over a holocaust of victims.

Colliers working in small levels smoked cigarettes and pipes, an indication that the place of work was thought to be 'more or less' gas free; many individual deaths and severe burnings did, however, occur in these small mines by small pockets of gas ignited by smoking and naked flame lights, which were used. Cats and dogs were used for the detection of blackdamp, but mainly dogs. Animal cruelty was sometimes found, as some people just did not care for the animals' wellbeing and safety. Domesticated rats and mice were also carried when canaries began to be used.

More than any others, they are the forgotten men of the coal industry, their deaths, slow and agonising, were so commonplace they were sometimes not even reported in the newspapers. Yet, as much as any other miners who met their deaths through mining, the victims of pneumoconiosis gave up their lives for coal. 'They just finish work and that was the end of them', said Sandra Bushen, of Penyrheol, near Caerphilly. She should know. Mrs Bushen has lost two close relatives to pneumoconiosis. Her family history has long been scarred by pit tragedy. She is the granddaughter of John Lewis, the man whose body lay underground for six weeks, following the 1913 disaster at Senghenydd. But it is coal dust disease that has blighted her family in more recent times. Her father-in-law Edward Bushen, of Trecenydd, started work at Bedwas Colliery when he was eleven years old. His fifty-one years at the pit cost him his health and ultimately his life. 'We had to watch my father-in-law suffer', recalled Mrs Bushen. 'He worked for fifty-one years, but when he came out he never had any payment or anything for it. He really suffered; it was pitiful to see him. Like so many of them, they just finish work and that's the end of them'. Mrs Bushen's uncle, William Lewis, also succumbed to pneumoconiosis, after overcoming an horrific pit accident. 'My uncle had a bad time in the pits. He was Senghenydd born and bred and worked at the Windsor Colliery in Abertridwr. It was at Markham colliery that he had an accident when a block of coal fell from the seam and severed his leg nearly in two'. Mr Lewis eventually retuned to work after eighteen months, but it was his lungs rather than his leg, which finally gave way. He died of pneumoconiosis on 15 March 1976.

There are few substances in nature more unprepossessing in appearance than coal, few, gleaming with a ruddy light on winter eves that are more attractive. Similarly, if the theme has a hard, repellent look, let us see if it cannot be made interesting and have an instructive influence as well. Widespread in its location, coal may be assumed to have a place in the language of most nations.

It is the *gahal* of the Hebrew, the *glo* of the old Briton, the *anthrax* of the Greek, the *carbo* of the Roman, the *coll* of the Saxon, the *kohle* of the Teuton and his Dutch and German descendant and the *charbon de terre* of that vivacious neighbour of ours opposite, the Frenchman.

There are twenty-eight references to coal in the Old and New Testaments and these show conclusively that its uses were as well known and as varied as now.

British historians generally concur in the opinion that coal was well known here before the arrival of the Romans and was used by workers in brass. The Britons knew coal by the primitive name of *glo* – and the use of coal by the Romans in Wales was proved by an interesting discovery of a Roman villa near Caerleon.

In the thirteenth century coal was being turned out at Llanfabon, the monks of Neath and Margam were similarly employed and very likely used it for their temporal good. Another claim for ancient coal working is Swansea, the Norman lord William de Breos AD 1305, 'empowering the tenant to dig Pit coal at Byllywasted, without the hindrance of ourselves or heirs'. In the centre of the old Norman castles of the thirteenth and fourteenth centuries stood the smithy who was our earliest ironmaster who used coal as well as charcoal in his labour at Morlais Castle.

The primitive mode of working in Elizabethan days was to drive a level and when they found the coal they worked holes, one for every digger, each miner working with candlelight, they had boys that carried the coal in baskets on their backs to the entrance and they worked from 6.00 a.m. to 6.00 p.m. every day. These primitive operations did not extend much beyond the scratching of the surface and it was not until the closing decades of the eighteenth century that coal mining as a settled industry sprang into being in this area. This was due to the utilisation of coal for smelting iron, a development in which the first John Guest, of Dowlais – the founder of a family destined to play a large part in the industrial and commercial life of Glamorganshire – was a pioneer.

In the opening of the nineteenth century coal was worked on a considerable scale in the Merthyr and Dowlais areas, the output being in excess of the iron-smelting needs of the time and there are records of a proportion of that excess finding its way down to Cardiff and over mountain tracks into Herefordshire. Towards the middle of the nineteenth century a few far-seeing men, outside the coterie of ironmasters, apprehended the immense values connoted on the new term, 'South Wales Smokeless Steam Coal', a term which within a short period was to attain and establish a standard of coal value the whole world over and men set to work as pioneers in beginnings so humble and difficulties so immense that no one who reads the story of their work can withhold a tribute to their courage and their faith.

In an endeavour to assist in eliminating any errors, help is requested from anyone willing to share their knowledge relating to the correct particulars of any relations or persons which may be incorrectly entered in this book.

Appendices

A Reality: There Were no Greater Mineral Treasures than the Riches of Coal

There were no greater mineral treasures than the riches of coal found by man as he searched the farthest recesses for Golden Nuggets which were in such abundance in the valleys of the South Wales Coalfield.

If you are male, then 100 years ago, or even fifty, you could have spent your working life underground. If oxygen was your most vital need, it was followed closely by artificial light in pitch blackness of a colliery. The darkness of a mine is indescribable. You push your hand out to feel it and your hand goes through solid blackness. There is no gleam of light or even relief of shadow. The darkness weighs on a man; it is as much torture to the eyes as blinding light.

Candles were one of the first forms of artificial light used underground. An Indian proverb says: A candle is a protest at darkness. It says 'in the darkness I beg to differ'. Some were made of animal fat. Regular catastrophic explosions spelled the end for naked flames, however, although there was resistance to the safety lamp. The problem was that until the end of the nineteenth century the safety lamp gave far poorer light than a candle. Colliers were paid by their output, so less light meant less coal. They also had to pay for their own lamps at first. Legislation in 1911 outlawed naked flame in deep mines, where gas was more likely, although miners continued to use it until the 1930s. Like chapel on Sunday, safety lamps have lit the path for Welsh miners and protected them from harm. Light is the miner's most precious friend in the subterranean blackness and also his worst enemy. The risk of a naked flame igniting methane gas was a constant threat in the coal mines. Many miners were killed by firedamp explosions, like that at Senghenydd on Tuesday 14 October 1913 when 439 men and boys died. A miner's life, his income and welfare are intricately bound to the light used in the pits. Mining was the bedrock of South Wales, employing 230,000 men producing 57 million tons of coal a year at its height in 1913. But the history of mining in Wales, which dates to pre-Roman times, also includes slate, lead, ironstone, copper and gold.

For centuries the only light came from tallow candles which were pushed into nooks and crannies or secured on a miner's hat with a lump of clay. Some mine owners supplied the candles; other sold them at a profit. To save money miners made their own from waste animal fat. Candles posed problems, least of which was that the rats ate them. On the other hand they kept miner John Evans alive when he ate them while trapped underground for twelve days in 1819. Candles were used until the end of the nineteenth century in non-coal mines, but they could not be safely used in many coal mines where inflammable methane gas lurks in the deeper coal seams.

A series of tragic firedamp explosions led scientist Sir Humphry Davy to invent the first oil-fired flame safety lamp in the Christmas of 1815, the best present a miner could have.

A Coal Miner's Safety Lamp

The Davy lamp incorporated a wire grille around the flame which absorbed the heat and reduced the chance of explosion. Improved design gave mines the Clanny lamp in 1839 which used a glass cylinder to protect the flame, and the Marsaut lamp in 1871, in which a metal bonnet replaced the wire grille. From the 1850s onward the gassy steam coal collieries of South Wales turned increasingly to the safety lamp, prompted by disasters like the firedamp explosion at Llanerch Colliery in Afon Lwyd Valley, Monmouthshire which killed 176 men and boys in 1890. An explosion four months earlier prompted the inspector of mines to urge the introduction of safe lamps. The colliery manager refused, with tragic results. Despite the advantages of safety lamps, many Welsh miners had to buy their own and thus resisted their introduction.

By the 1930s electric hand lamps became common in the coalmines, to be replaced by helmet-mounted electric cap lamps following nationalisation of the coal industry. The advent of battery-powered electric lights led to a dramatic drop in cases of miners' nystagmus, an eye disease caused by working in poor light.

Slate and metal mines took to carbide lamps at the turn of the nineteenth century. The lamps worked by dripping water onto calcium carbide to crate a flame. By the 1950s carbide lamps were abandoned in favour of electric cap lamps. The familiar miners' safety lamp is still in use. At the start of every shift a colliery official goes round the mine with a safety lamp testing for methane which creates a blue cap over the flame. An explosion is caused by the ignition of combustible firedamp gas (a mixture of methane [predominant], carbon monoxide, nitrogen, ethane, carbon dioxide) and air.

Justice for the Miners

In 1952 a demonstration took place in Cardiff demanding justice for victims of pneumoconiosis. A survey of the Rhondda Valley in the same year revealed that more than half the miners had this disease. One in five suffered its severest and most deadly form.

A Great Mountain Colliery Lodge Banner at this demonstration read:

Mountain of Despair. Valley of Gloom.

Pneumoconiosis the deadly dust.
They toiled to dig the nation's coal and breathed the deadly dust.
Betrayed once more. Denied the dole by those who held their trust.
They are not here amidst the throng their health is too impaired.
We march for them to right the wrong so that they may be spared.

The symptoms of pneumoconiosis are as follows: dyspnoea (shortness of breath); cough is almost always present; sputum (phlegm) is, as a rule, scanty but may be copious (plentiful) and black. In late stages there may be signs of heart failure or tuberculosis. Justice will never be rendered.

Yore Times of Coal in the Holy Bible: Authorised King James Version

1. LEVETICUS 16:12: And he shall take a censer full of burning coals of fire from off the altar before the LORD, and his hands full of sweet incense beaten small, and bring it within the veil.
2. 2 SAMUEL 14:7: And, behold, the whole family is risen against thine handmaid, and they said, Deliver him that smote his brother, that we may kill him, for the life of his brother whom he slew; and we will destroy the heir also: and so they shall quench my coal which is left, and shall not leave to by husband neither name nor reminder upon the earth.
3. 2 SAMUEL 22:9: There went up a smoke out of his nostrils, and fire out of his mouth devoured: coals were kindled by it.
4. 2 SAMUEL 22:13: Through the brightness before him were coals of fire kindled.
5. 1 KINGS 19:6: And he looked, and, behold, there was a cake baken on the coals, and a cruse of water at his head. And he did eat and drink, and laid him down again.
6. JOB 41:21: His breath kindleth coals, and a flame goeth out of his mouth.
7. PSALM 18:8: There went up a smoke out of his nostrils, and fire out of his mouth devoured: coals were kindled by it.
8. PSALM 18:12: At the brightness that was before him his thick clouds passed, hail stones and coals of fire.
9. PSALM 18:13: The LORD also thundered in the heavens, and the Highest gave his voice; hail stones and coals of fire.
10. PSALM 120:4: Sharp arrows of the mighty, with coals of juniper.
11. PSALM 140:10: Let burning coals fall upon them: let them be cast into the fire; into deep pits, that they rise not up again.

12. PROVERBS 6:28: Can one go upon hot coals, and his feet not be burned?

13. PROVERBS 25:22: For thou shalt heap coals of fire upon his head, and the LORD shall reward thee.

14. PROVERBS 26:2 1: As coals are to burning coals, and wood to fire; so it is contentious man to kindle strife.

15. SONG OF SOLOMON 8:6: Set me as a sea! Upon thine heart, as a seal upon thine arm: for love is strong as death; jealousy is cruel as the grave: the coals thereof are coals of fire, which hath a most vehement flame.

16. ISAIAH 6:6: Then flew one of the seraphims unto me, having a live coal in his hand, which he had taken with the tongs from off the altar.

17. ISAIAH 44:12: The smith with the tongs both worketh in the coals, and fashioneth it with hammers, and worketh it with the strength of his arms: yea, he is hungry, and his strength faileth: he drinketh no water, and is faint.

18. ISAIAH 44:19: And none considereth in his heart, neither is there knowledge nor understanding to say, I have burned part of it in the fire; yea, also I have baked bread upon the coals thereof; I have roasted flesh, and eaten it: and shall I make the residue thereof an abomination? Shall I fall down to the stock of a tree?

19. ISAIAH 47:14: Behold, they shall be as stubble; the fire shall burn them; they shall not deliver themselves from the power of the flame: there shall not be a coal to warm at, nor fire to sit before it.

20. ISAIAH 54:16: Behold, I have created the smith that bloweth the coals in the fire, and that bringeth forth an instrument for his work; and I have created the waster to destroy.

21. LAMENTATIONS 4:8: Their visage is blacker than a coal; they are not known in the streets: their skin cleaveth to their bones; it is withered, it is become like a stick.

22. EZEKIEL 1:13: As for the likeness of the living creatures, their appearance was like burning coals of fire, and like the appearance of lamps: it went up and down among the living creatures; and the fire was bright, and out of the fore went forth lightning.

23. EZEKIEL 10:2: And he spake unto the man clothed with linen, and said, Go in between the wheels, even under the cherub, and fill thy hands with coals of fire from between the cherubims, and scatter them over the city. And he went in in my sight.

24. EZEKIEL 24:11: Then set it empty upon the coals thereof, that the brass of it may be hot, and may burn, and that the filthiness of it may be molten in it, that the scum of it may be consumed.

25. HABAKKUK 3:5: Before him went the pestilence, and burning coals went forth at his feet.

26. SAINT JOHN 18:18: And the servants and officers stood there, who had made a fire of coals; for it was cold: and they warmed themselves: and Peter stood with them, and warmed himself.

27. SAINT JOHN 21:9: As soon then as they were came to land, they saw a fire of coals there, and fish laid thereon, and bread.

28. ROMANS 12:20: Therefore IF THINE ENEMY HUNGER, FEED HIM; IF HE THIRST, GIVE HIM DRINK: FOR IN SO DOING THOU SHALT HEAP COALS OF FIRE ON HIS HEAD.

The Psalms, which are a perfect storehouse of historic fact, giving insight into social life amongst the Jews, their handicraft and customs, refer to fuel in a manner suggestive that, though coal was known, the chief fuel was that of wood. 'He scattereth the hoar frost like ashes. Who shall withstand his frost'. The ashes of the Six-Feet and the Nine-Feet coal seams are white compared with those of bituminous coal, but the ashes of wood unquestionably come nearer to the psalmist's description.

Inspector of Coal Mines Report, 1896

It is to be hoped the Order which you recently made under the powers conferred by section 6 of the new Act as to explosives will be the means of improving the safety of mining in this important district. Its effect will be to shut out common blasting powder and gelatine dynamite from practically all coal mines. I am hopeful that owners, managers and workmen will loyally accept the conditions of the order without demur and that it will further have the effect of stimulating everyone concerned in the lessening of the use of any explosive whatever in all mines where danger exists from either firedamp or coal dust. J.T. Robson, Inspector of Coal Mines.

Explosion at Cambrian Colliery

Report on the causes of, and circumstances attending, the
Explosion, which occurred at Cambrian Colliery,
Glamorganshire, on 17th May 1965
by H.S. Stephenson, B.Sc., M.I.Min, E. HM Chief Inspector of Mines and Quarries.
Presented to parliament by the Minister of Power by Command of Her Majesty November 1965.

The Right Honourable Frederick Lee, MP   30th September 1965.
Minister of Power.

Sir,

1. In accordance with your direction, I held a Public Inquiry with respect to the accident which occurred at Cambrian Colliery in the County of Glamorgan on 17th May, 1965. The names, ages and occupations of the 31 persons who were killed and the one person seriously injured in the accident are given at the end of the report.

2. I opened the Inquiry in the Law Courts, Cardiff, on 19th July, 1965, and it lasted four days, during which fifty-eight persons gave evidence.

3. The interested parties were represented as follows: The Ministry of Power, by Mr Cyril Leigh, HM Divisional Inspector of Mines and Quarries for the South Western Division, with Dr E.M. Guénault, Deputy Director of the Safety in Mines Research Establishment.

The National Coal Board, by Dr H.L. Willett, Deputy Director General of Production (Safety and Techniques), with Mr G.S. Morgan, Production Director of the South Western Division of the National Coal Board, and Mr G. Blackmore, Area General Manager of the No.3 Area in that Division.

The National Union of Mineworkers, by Mr W. Whitehead, President of the South Wales Area, with Mr L. James of the Union's Safety Department in the Area.

The National Association of Colliery Overmen, Deputies and Shotfirers, by Mr E. White,
President of the South Wales Area, with Mr W.D. Jones, District Secretary, and Mr M. Harcombe, Lodge Secretary, Cambrian Colliery.

The National Association of Colliery Managers and the British Association of Colliery Management, by Sir Andrew Bryan, Mining Engineer, with Mr W. Humphrey, Electrical Engineer, and Mr J. Pocock, Mining Engineer.

4. My findings are that:
(1). the casualties were caused by an explosion which occurred just before 1:00 p.m. in the P26 District in the Pentre coal seam;
(2). the explosion was almost entirely one of firedamp, flame spreading along about 325 yards of face and return roadway and coal dust playing no significant part;
(3). the firedamp involved was emitted into the airway from strata other than the seam being worked and assumed explosive proportions because of a severe reduction in the ventilation circulating the district;
(4). this reduction resulted from a prolonged short-circuit through two access holes in an air bridge (or air crossing) and from a connection with previous workings; and
(5). the firedamp was ignited by an electric arc within a gate-end switch, which electricians were testing while the front cover was unbolted.

General Description

The Colliery.

5. Cambrian Colliery, in the No.3 Area of the National Coal Board's South Western Division, is situated near the village

of Clydach Vale in the Borough of Rhondda, some 20 miles north-west of Cardiff. There are four shafts; No.1 Shaft, a downcast sixteen feet in diameter, sunk to the Five-Feet coal seam at a depth of 506 yards, the present winding level being at the Pentre coal seam inset at a depth of 212 yards; the Maindy Shaft, at the former Colliery of that name, elliptical 14 feet by 12 feet, serving as the upcast for the Pentre coal seam workings; and No.3 and No.4 Shafts, used for workings in the Five-Feet, Lower Nine-Feet and Bute coal seams. The Maindy Shaft was equipped with a radial flow fan producing 103,000 cubic feet per minute at 48 inches of water gauge.

Management.

6. The principal officials were:

Area General Manager G. Blackmore

Area Production Manager G. Hodkin

Deputy Area Production Manager (operations) J.J. Lewis

Deputy Area Production Manager (planning) W.J. Strong

Group Manager E. Pugh

Manager E. Breeze

Undermanager No.1 Pit L. Williams

Both Mr. Breeze and Mr. Williams were killed in the explosion.

Output and Persons Employed.

7. The Colliery employed 816 men at the time of the incident, 654 below ground and 162 on the surface, and the daily output was 700 tons from the Pentre coal seam and 300 tons from the Lower Nine-Feet and Bute coal seams. The Colliery has always been a safety-lamp mine and had a lamp room of the 'self-service' type equipped with 770 cap lamps, 129 flame safety lamps, of which 59 were of the internal re-lighter type, and eight automatic firedamp detectors.

The Pentre Coal Seam.

8. The general layout of the present underground workings in the Pentre coal seam and the system of ventilation. The coal seam, 240 yards deep at the shaft and three feet thick, is overlain by the Pentre Rider coal seam some 24 feet above, coal measure shales and sandstone separating the two coal seams. Beneath the Pentre coal seam, at a distance of 41 feet, is the Lower Pentre coal seam, beds of sandstone, one 19 feet thick, and mudstone separating these two coal seams.

P26 District
General.

9. Plan No.1 (not included), the Incident Plan, shows details of the condition in which the P26 District was found after the explosion.

10. The district, situated some 3,000 yards from the No.1 Pit bottom, was in effect a continuation of the P25 District which had of necessity to be stopped as it approached the main return airway known as the Maindy Heading Return. It was formed by extending the P25 Conveyor Road as a coal heading over the Maindy Heading Return, while at the same time a short drift rising at a gradient of 1 in 24, parallel to the coal heading, was driven from the Maindy Heading Return to intersect the seam. The two roads were then connected to form a face which came into full production in January, 1965. At the time of the incident, the face was 192 yards long and was advancing to the north on a rising gradient of 1 in 33, while the gradient across the face was rising at 1 in 17 from the intake gate.

11. The face machinery consisted of a rapid plough worked in conjunction with an armoured face conveyor, both electrically driven. The intake gate (or conveyor roadway), supported by 12 feet by 8 feet arch girders, had a coal rib on the right side and an eight yard wide pack on the left. The return gate (or supply roadway), supported by 10 feet

by 8 feet arch girders, had a coal rib on the left side and an eight yard wide pack on the right. Rippings to form the roadways were taken in two sections, each approximately three feet six inches thick, the front sections just in advance of the face line, and the main sections normally in line with the packs. The stables at each end of the face were 18 feet wide. Coal getting was carried out on the day and afternoon shifts on alternate weeks; the front sections of the rippings were invariably taken on the night shift, and the main sections on the other non-coaling shifts.

Support on the Face.
12. The face was open caved and a 'prop-free front' system of support was employed using hand-set hydraulic props contained in pairs of frames. set at five feet intervals, each pair consisting of one frame with three props and the other with two. The frames in each pair were advanced alternately. The areas immediately in front of the gate side packs were supported by hydraulic props with metre long link bars, and the roadheads by 11 feet long straight steel girders, each set on three props.

Transport.
13. Coal from the face was delivered by an armoured conveyor on to a chain conveyor in the intake gate, which in turn delivered on to a second chain conveyor and thence on to a 30 inch wide belt conveyor. At a loading point some 800 yards outbye the coal was transferred to 30 hundredweight drams and taken by rope haulage to the No.1 Shaft bottom. Supplies for the district were brought from the No.1 Shaft along the main haulage road and then by way of a road, named MacBains, into the Maindy Heading Return and thence into the district.

Explosives.
14. Pulsed infusion shotfiring was practised in the stables while the rippings were brought down by Eq. S. explosives.

Ventilation.
15. The district was ventilated by a separate split, from the main intake, which crossed over the Maindy Heading Return at an air crossing, locally known as an air bridge, a term I shall use in the remainder of this Report. On leaving the face, the air passed down the return gate into the Maindy Heading Return, under the air bridge, and thence to the Maindy Upcast Shaft. Near the outbye end of the split was a pair of ventilation doors, to which I shall refer later. The last statutory ventilation measurements taken on 26th April, 1965, while the face was in full production, show that the quantities of air available outbye the air bridge and circulating the face were 23,000 cubic feet per minute and 8,000 cubic feet per minute respectively. An air sample taken at about the same time ten yards from the face in the return gate contained 0.38 per cent of firedamp.

The Air Bridge.
16. The details of the construction of the air bridge which that there were two openings in the floor of the bridge, one approximately nine square feet and covered with loose boards and the other approximately four square feet and covered with a corrugated sheet. Apart from the openings, the floor of the air bridge was formed by wood boards inserted into the flanges of straight girders, the intervening space to the top of the girders being filled with small dirt.

Precautions against Coal Dust.
17. The last statutory road dust samples were taken in April, 1965, and the records of their analysis show that the incombustible content varied between 66 and 77 per cent. These figures are well in the excess of the 55 per cent statutorily required for a coal seam, such as the Pentre, having a volatile content of 20·25 per cent.

Automatic Firedamp Detectors.
18. At the time of the explosion automatic firedamp detectors were not in use in the district, nor was there any evidence to suggest that they ever had been.

General Experience.

19. The district had been in full production for only four months at the time of the explosion, but during that time work seems to have proceeded without undue incident. There had been some difficulty arising from the fact that the props were a little too long for the working height at the face, but the management had decided to replace them and this was being done. When the face started it was parallel to the Maindy Heading Return and so not at right angles to the intake and return gates. From the outset, the return end of the face had been advanced more rapidly than the intake end so as to bring it into line at right angles with the roads, and this had almost been achieved at the time of the explosion. The effect of this procedure, however, was to distort the line of the face and to create a situation whereby the return roadside pack did not always keep pace with the advance of the face. At the time of the explosion this pack was about eight yards behind, hence the air leaving the face could not sweep into the fast end. In spite of the reduction in packing, support of the roof in this area by chocks and props appeared to be adequate.

20. Although it was said that the management intended to complete the air bridge by providing a concrete floor, this had not been done. Further, the access holes were, in the beginning, regarded as no more than a temporary expedient pending the drivage of a proper connection between the intake gate and the Maindy Heading Return. Although this had been started, other work was accorded a higher priority and the drivage of the connection was discontinued. It is quite understandable that the evidence about the way the access holes were used was not always entirely consistent because witnesses passed the air bridge at different times and saw it in differing conditions, but I was left with the impression that the smaller of the two holes, which was equipped with a ladder, was open for most of the time, if indeed it was not permanently open. The larger of the two holes was used to facilitate the passage of bulky materials, although up to the day of the explosion this appears to have been relatively infrequent and then only for periods of up to about an hour. The loose covering boards did not, however, provide a good seal.

21. In the course of the Inquiry many references were made to the pair of ventilation doors near the outbye end of the split. The evidence concerning their purpose was somewhat conflicting, but I think it would be right to say that they were originally provided in connection with the ventilation of the P25 face. When that face ceased production the doors were kept open except for the few occasions when it was necessary to deflect air into the P25 District when salvage operations were in progress there. They were simply regulators and in fact any air deflected into P25 would have rejoined the main current outbye of the air bridge. Opened or closed, they could have had little effect on subsequent events.

22. On 7th May, the intake end of the face made contact with the right hand roadhead of the old P11 District. The connection was made at the end of the coaling shift and the deputy took immediate steps to close the small opening with brattice cloth. In succeeding shifts brattice sheets were erected in the old roadway and on the Tuesday, six days before the explosion, T. Evans, a mason, began to construct a wood and cloth stopping with a door across the old roadway near to the holing. Because of a shortage of materials, the work on the door was not completed by the week-end, and so, on the Monday morning. Evans, having acquired the necessary materials, went in to close off the remaining area of about one square yard of the stopping. He completed the work by 11:15 a.m. and then left the district.

The Shifts Before The Explosion
14th–17th May.

23. The last coaling shift before that on which the explosion occurred was the afternoon of Friday, 14th May. The deputy in charge, B. Pyne, who was a substitute for the regular shift deputy, said that the shift was normal and that he did not detect firedamp in the course of his inspections. He recalled that sometime during the shift the access holes in the air bridge were open for the passage of materials, but he did not observe any adverse effect on the ventilation.

24. The next shift to which I need to refer is that of the night shift of 16th/17th May. The deputy, C. Evans, had in his charge a few men who were engaged in changing props on the face. He said that supplies were not brought into the district during the night shift and that the shift was normal in all respects.

The Morning Shift of 17th May.

25. The day shift of 17th May went underground at the usual time and arrived in the district at about 7:30 a.m. H. Pope was the district overman and T.E. Davies was the deputy in charge. Apart from work on the face that morning, there was a considerable amount of other activity in the district. Two major operations were in progress, firstly, the transport and erection of a belt conveyor in the intake gate to replace one of the existing chain conveyors and, secondly, the extension of a rope haulage system in the return gate. As a consequence of these activities the number of men in the district was greatly in excess of the normal complement. A. Richards and P. Best, two repairers, who spent the whole of the shift at or near the air bridge, were engaged in getting parts for the conveyor drive head up through the larger of the two access holes from the Maindy Heading Return for D. Bessant and E.L.T. Jones, fitters, who, with others, were erecting the conveyor. They removed the boards covering the larger opening at about 8:30 am., but shortly afterwards Overman Pope visited them and noted that, although the access hole was open, the materials to be passed through were not there. He gave instructions for the hole to be closed until the materials were on the spot, and the men replaced the boards while they went along the Maindy Heading Return to load machinery parts into drams. This probably took one-half to three-quarters of an hour, but it seems clear that, from the time the material reached the air bridge until the explosion, the larger access hole remained open. According to Richards, the other access hole, the smaller one equipped with a ladder, remained open throughout the shift and other witnesses confirmed this.

27. The day shift pit overman, G. Price, said that it was normal practice for the smaller of the two access holes to be open throughout the coaling shift and his understanding was that the other access hole would have been open for at least half of the shift that morning. The deputy, Davies, said that he found the larger access hole open and the two men engaged in raising machinery through it when he returned to the air bridge on the completion of his first inspection at 10:20 a.m. He said he was satisfied with the state of the ventilation throughout the whole of his shift. Other persons who passed by way of the air bridge during the morning had varying recollections about the openings, but they were generally consistent with those of the men primarily concerned.

28. The extension of the rope haulage in the return gate involved the transfer of a number of sheave wheels from one side of the gate to the other. R.C. Jones, sheavesman for the mine, who was supervising this work, was in the roadway for nearly three hours from 9:30 a.m. and thought the ventilation satisfactory. As he was coming out of the road at about 12:15 p.m., two electricians passed him going inbye.

29. Another item of work which had a bearing on the subsequent events was the completion of the door and stopping in the P11 connection. This, as I have already recounted, was effected at 11:15 a.m.

30. Although coaling commenced normally, it was interrupted at about 9:00 a.m. by the breaking of the plough chain, which seems to have coincided with a failure of the face telephone circuit. The chain was repaired by about 11:00 a.m. and coaling recommenced after food time, the telephone circuit in the meantime having been repaired by electricians. At some time, possibly just before 12 noon, a shot was fired in the return stable and the coal filled out.

31. According to overman Price, who had spent over an hour supervising the repair of the plough chain, signalling trouble developed on the face at about 11:50 a.m. and ploughing was again interrupted. The fault on the signalling system either cleared itself or was rectified by someone unknown. There was some contradiction in the evidence about whether or not ploughing recommenced but, if it did, it could only have been for a few minutes because at about 12:15 p.m. an electrical fault developed at the return end plough motor. The overman telephoned K. Davies, the plough operator at the return end, who told him that the electricians were working on the switches in the return gate with one panel open but that the fault had not been located. Price then gave instructions for the plough to be brought down the face by the motor at the intake end; this was done but attempts to plough back up the face were unsuccessful.

32. When the electrical fault developed the deputy was on his way along the face towards the intake end, and at about 12:40 p.m., when some 40 yards from the intake gate, he encountered the manager and the undermanager. They told him that overman Price was attending to the electrical fault, but after a few minutes the manager instructed the deputy to go and find out what was happening. Davies went to the telephone at the intake end of the face and spoke to the plough operator at the return end, who said he would go and make enquiries. While the deputy was waiting at the telephone, the explosion occurred.

The Explosion

33. As nearly as can be estimated, the time was then 12:55 p.m. The deputy was struck by violent blast which blew him backwards, but he did not recollect seeing any flame. Overman Price, who was on his way to a telephone between the face and the air bridge, was blown over into the side of the road by the blast. He immediately went back to the face where, he met the deputy and others but, because of smoke and dust, visibility was severely restricted. With the deputy, he then went to the outbye telephone and raised the alarm. Shortly afterwards, D. Jones, at the loading point outbye, was instructed to go into P23 District to fetch the men from there to assist in rescue operations; this he did and then went inbye along the P26 intake gate passing through the ventilation doors, which were closed, and over the air bridge, both access holes of which he noted were open. Some little time later, Best, acting on instructions, propped open the ventilation doors.

34. The overman, the deputy and a number of men, who had been in the intake and survived the explosion, then attempted rescue operations pending the arrival of the Rescue Brigade. Realising the impossibility of going on to the face from the intake end, they went down the ladder at the air bridge into the Maindy Heading Return and along to the junction with the return gate from the face. The overman penetrated into the return gate for a matter of about ten yards but was wisely prevailed upon not to proceed further. T. Rees, a rider, working in the Maindy Heading Return, who had suffered serious injury, was given first aid by the deputy.

35. The Porth Central Mines Rescue Station was alerted at 1:05 p.m. and the Brigade arrived at the pit at 1:17 p.m. A team composed of permanent Brigade members captained by L.C. Lewis and accompanied by the superintendent, J. Perry, went down the pit at 1:25 p.m. arriving in the affected district at 2:10 p.m. When the team entered the face from the intake gate at 2:20 p.m., they found the atmosphere very smoky and dusty but gradually it cleared. Having been instructed to be back at base by 3:00 p.m. the team had soon to leave the face and return. Lewis then led the team into the face a second time and they reached the mid-point on the face before turning back. There was still a great deal of dust in the atmosphere. Thereafter rescue operations proceeded with other teams; in due course the atmosphere cleared and the bodies of the victims were recovered.

The Investigation

General.

36. With the completion of recovery operations, a preliminary examination of the district was undertaken by H.M. Inspectorate of Mines and Quarries. This examination indicated that the explosion had affected the face and the return gate. To establish the cause of the explosion, H.M. Inspectors and scientists of the Safety in Mines Research Establishment (S.M.R.E.), with every assistance from the representatives of management and workpeople, then engaged in an intensive examination of the district, in the course of which a number of pieces of equipment and many samples of articles and materials were collected and later subjected to laboratory examination.

The Extent of Flame and Blast.

37. From the results of the examination it was concluded that flame had passed along 325 yards of face and associated roadway and that about double this distance had been subjected to blast.

The Intake Gate.

38. Over a length of roadway 30-50 yards from the main ripping there was a partly built stone dust barrier. Some of the frames of this had been displaced, but this was the only sign of violence in the roadway outbye the main ripping. A great deal of coal dust spillage from the conveyor was observed, but the road had not recently been stone dusted nearer than 15 yards outbye from the main ripping. Nevertheless, there were no signs of heating or coking in this part of the gate. Between the main ripping and the face there was evidence of mild blast in an outbye direction and of very slight coking, but none of heating on the collected samples. Appreciable amounts of post explosion dust were found particularly on surfaces facing inbye, and also in the old P11 road. In this road there were, however, no signs of burning, coking or blast.

The Face.

39. Of the samples collected in the face working area only a few items, such as safety helmets, bore evidence of blast or heating. There were moderate deposits of dust in the half of the face adjacent to the intake gate and heavier deposits in the other half, particularly on surfaces facing the return end. Examination of samples indicated some degree of coking, mainly at the return end of the face.

The Return Gate Roadhead.

40. In the face of the return stable there was a four feet eight inch deep uncharged shot hole, two feet from the left hand side, while five feet six inches to the right of this was a socket, 11 inches deep and 12 inches in diameter, containing fine damp coal. There was no loose coal in the stable. There were indications of heavy burning on a number of wood splinters and plastic covered wire, and of heavy coking on the outbye sides of props. Moderately heavy deposits of post explosion dust were observed on the rib side wall of the stable, and there were distinct signs of blast in an inbye direction.

The Return Gate.

41. Four flameproof gate-end switches were mounted on a trolley at a point 11 yards outbye the main ripping in the return gate. The hinged cover of the one nearest the face, which controlled the return end plough motor, was not securely closed as none of its ten bolts was in position; they were found lying on the apparatus or nearby. The three-pin control cable connection at the back of the switch was disconnected. After the switch had been removed for testing, a damaged rectifier was found under the left hand rail of the track immediately below the position of the switch. A few feet farther outbye, also on trolleys, were two flameproof motors and two hydraulic pumps and tanks. A single-shot exploder and a six-shot exploder were found in this area. There were signs of heavy burning for about 32 yards outbye the main ripping lip. Throughout the length of the return gate explosion dust was observed and there were clear signs of coking.

42. At a point 24 yards down the return gate from the main ripping, a vacuum flask impacted into the outbye end of a wooden prop, one of a horizontal stack, gave an indication of the violence. At 124 yards, a tub had been overturned, and at 140 yards, an arch girder had been displaced in an outbye direction. Over the next 21 yards three more arches had been similarly displaced, and near the junction with the Maindy Heading Return strong indications of blast in an outbye direction were observed.

Maindy Heading Return.

43. Indications of blast were found in the Maindy Heading Return for about 65 yards of the roadway inbye of the junction with the P26 Return Gate; shattered pieces of brattice cloth and wood were found strewn about. In the roadway outbye of the junction, there were signs of violence for a distance of 55 yards. There was no evidence of heating and little post explosion dust in the 120 yards of the Maindy Heading Return which had been affected by blast.

Electrical Apparatus

General.

44. Electricity for the district was supplied from two mobile flameproof air-cooled transformers situated in the Maindy Heading Return, one just inbye the junction with P26 Return Gate and the other near the air bridge. In the intake gate outbye the air bridge were two switches controlling the motors of one of the chain conveyors in that gate. Farther inbye were four other gate-end switches controlling motors for the other chain conveyor, the face conveyor and the plough. In addition there was one spare switch with a test plug in the socket. There was also a signalling transformer. In the return gate close to the roadhead were four gate-end switches controlling motors for a ram pump, a chock pump, the face conveyor and the plough. The two plough motors were arranged for simultaneous working. The face was equipped with sound powered telephones for communication between the gate ends, and with a face signalling system.

Examination in the Pit.

45. All the electrical apparatus and associated cables were examined in situ by H.M. Electrical Inspector of Mines and Quarries. He found the switches on both the transformers and the isolators on all the gate-end switches in the return gate in the 'Off' position, but it was later disclosed that they had been switched off soon after the explosion as a safety measure. With one exception all the apparatus was found to be in a satisfactory condition. Nevertheless, a number of pieces, including the signalling equipment, were withdrawn from the mine and sent to the S.M.R.E. for laboratory examination and test. Again, with the same exception, all were found to be in a satisfactory condition, being either intrinsically safe or flameproof as appropriate, with nothing to give rise to the suspicion that any one of them might have provided an igniting source. The exception was the gate-end switch in the return gate which supplied power to the return end plough motor.

The Switch Controlling the Plough Motor.

46. When this unit was examined, the sequence/independent switch was in the 'independent' position and the bypass/operate switch in the 'operate' position. The ten bolts of the cover were found lying on top of the switch or nearby; the cover itself was closed but with a flange gap of about one-quarter inch at the side opposite the hinges. The bolted plug of the control cable had been withdrawn from the back of the switch, leaving the pins exposed. Inside the switch it was noted that the earth leakage and the proving relays had been removed and these were later found on the floor nearby. To complete the circuits, pieces of wire had been inserted in the sockets provided for these relays, and the stop switch contacts had been bridged with a piece of V.I.R. cable. When later examined in the laboratory at the S.M.R.E. no signs of heating on any component within the enclosure were immediately visible, but microscopic examination disclosed particles of coke and definite signs of burning, the latter especially on the string harness used for securing the relay connecting wires. With the isolator in the 'On' position, it was found that the cover could be opened three inches at the side opposite the hinges.

47. The switch was then subjected to flameproof testing in an explosion chamber with the hinged cover closed but not bolted, and with the isolator in the 'On' position. In these conditions a gap of 0·08 inch was measured between the enclosure and the cover. Ignition tests were then carried out with the chamber containing an explosively weak mixture of 59 per cent fire-damp in air. In each of two tests the external mixture was ignited and the cover was found to have opened to 11/16 of an inch at the side opposite the hinges. In further tests, using richer mixtures of seven or eight per cent of firedamp in air, the gap revealed after ignition was only 3/32 of an inch and the external inflammation was noticeably more violent. The smaller gap could have resulted from the partial re-closing of the cover by external pressure. During all the tests there was no violent movement of the cover and no mechanical damage to it or to the cover/isolator interlocking device.

Mechanical Apparatus.

48. All the mechanical apparatus in the district was examined by H.M. Inspector of Mechanical Engineering for signs

of frictional heating, frictional sparking, spontaneous ignition of oil vapour or any other likely source of ignition. Not only did he fail to discover any, but he found all the equipment to be in a satisfactory condition.

Safety Lamps.

49. Five flame safety lamps and 44 electric cap lamps recovered from the district were sent to the S.M.R.E. for examination and test. Only one, an electric cap lamp, was regarded as a possible igniting source, but it could not have caused the explosion because it was found at a point on the face near the intake end and the flame and blast pattern were totally inconsistent with an explosion having originated there.

Contraband.

50. Among the effects of one of the victims there were two cigarettes but no matches or lighters were found, either there or in the explosion area. I am entirely satisfied that contraband was not the cause of this explosion.

Road Dust Samples.

51. Dust samples were collected from the roof, sides and floor at 33 places in the district, three in the return gate, 15 in the intake gate and 15 in the Maindy Heading Return. Upon analysis, those from the return gate were found to be satisfactory, with percentages of incombustible content varying from 61 to 80 per cent. The others ranged from 22 to 91 per cent, 22 of them being under 55 per cent.

Ventilation

Air Quantities.

52. In two series of ventilation experiments made on 20th/21st May and on 4th June, H.M. Inspectors took measurements of the quantity of air passing certain points in the district in varying circumstances involving the opening and shutting of both the ventilation doors and the access holes in the air bridge. When the experiments took place the door into the old P11 District, which had been damaged in the explosion, had been repaired. Inspectors noted that the opening and shutting of the ventilation doors had little or no effect on the quantity of air reaching the air bridge and throughout the experiments this varied from 21,000 to 25,000 cubic feet per minute.

53. The opening and closing of the access holes in the air bridge, however, had a very significant effect on the ventilation inbye. With the holes closed, only 13,000 cubic feet of air per minute reached the intake roadhead. This in itself was indicative of the unsatisfactory condition of the air bridge. When the ladder way hole was open, the quantity of air reaching the intake roadhead fell to about 9,000 cubic feet per minute. When the other access hole was also opened, the quantity of air reaching the roadhead fell by a further 5,000 cubic feet per minute to about 4,000 cubic feet per minute. Further measurements disclosed that of these quantities, about 3,000 cubic feet per minute of air was being lost into P11 District, notwithstanding the presence in the road in that district of a door and sheets.

54. Coincident with these measurements other measurements were being taken in the return gate. These gave quantities of about 10,000 cubic feet per minute when both access holes in the air bridge were closed; about 6,000 cubic feet per minute when the ladder way was open; and about 1,000 cubic feet per minute when both access holes were open.

Firedamp.

55. In the course of other experiments, the S.M.R.E. found that at a point 120 yards outbye the main ripping lip in the return gate, with a ventilating current of about 7,500 cubic feet per minute (corresponding to a velocity of about 110 feet per minute) firedamp concentrations were present in small cavities over the crown of the arches, but that there was none in the gate itself. Later, when the velocity was reduced to 75 feet per minute (corresponding to a quantity of about 5.000 cubic feet per minute) by the opening of the ladder way, there was still no firedamp below the crown of the arches. When, however, the velocity fell to 20 feet per minute and the quantity to about 1.000 cubic feet per

minute, with both access holes in the air bridge open, firedamp appeared below the crown of the arches at the same place, and moved uphill against the ventilating current in the form of a continuous layer, in concentrations varying from five per cent upwards.

56. Inspectors found that in similar conditions, that is, when both access holes were open and the quantity of air passing was about 1,000 cubic feet per minute, in the space of two and a quarter hours a concentration of firedamp developed in the area of the switches with three and a half per cent concentration slightly above the middle of the roadway or just below the top of the switches. When the holes were closed, the accumulated firedamp dispersed in a matter of 20 minutes.

57. While these layers were forming in the return gate, no firedamp could be detected on a flame safety lamp inbye the main ripping lip in that gate. During the period of two and a quarter hours methanometer determinations, taken at distances of up to 14 feet into the waste at ten yard intervals along the face line, in no case exceeded 0·6 per cent. On the other hand, except for 0·15 per cent firedamp at the corner of the return gate roadside pack, no firedamp was detected either on the face or in the waste when the access holes in the air bridge were closed.

58. On four occasions, over a seven week period from the day of the explosion, during the whole of which time the face was idle, and when the quantity of air passing varied from 8,000 to 12,000 cubic feet per minute, determinations of the firedamp content in the general body of the return air were taken by the colliery management. These observations were taken at three stations, and the concentrations of firedamp were found to remain virtually constant during the period varying from 0·1 per cent at 20 yards from the face to 0·14 per cent at 70 yards and 0.4 per cent at 180 yards. Point of Ignition.

59. The blast and flame pattern disclosed by the investigation was in the S.M.R.E.'s view consistent with the explosion having originated in the return gate between the main ripping and a point 120 yards outbye of that ripping. Within this region the only possible source of ignition was the bank of gate-end switches located eleven yards outbye of the main ripping, one of which was the suspect switch to which I have already referred. Evidence of the conversation just before the explosion between overman Price and K. Davies, the plough operator who was one of the victims, indicated that immediately prior to it, two electricians were working on an open gate-end switch. From the condition in which this switch was found one can only conclude that a sequence of testing was being carried out to locate a fault while the power was on, and that this could have led to the closing of a contactor within the switch. As was explained at the Inquiry by H.M. Electrical Inspector the probability was that the electricians, in trying to locate the fault by elimination, might well have connected a rectifier between either the reverse or forward pin of the control circuit socket and earth. As the proving relay contacts had been bridged, the use of the rectifier would have resulted in the operation of the contactor. This could have caused heavy arcing, which in the view of the S.M.R.E. would have ignited any explosive mixture of firedamp and air. Their experiments leave no doubt that with the cover unbolted, flames within the switch would have been communicated to the external atmosphere. During the examination of the equipment a fault, which would have prevented the operation of the proving relay and consequently the motor itself, was found in the interlock circuit in the plug at the plough motor.

The Development of the Explosion.

60. It was the view of the S.M.R.E. that flame from within the gate-end switch ignited firedamp in its vicinity, the firedamp being in the form of a roof layer similar to the one obtained by experiment, with the possibility that in addition there may have been some accumulation in the stable area. Flame would then be propagated slowly both inbye and outbye probably along the lower inflammable fringe of the layer. The turbulence generated by pressure waves in advance of the flame would break up the firedamp layer producing a highly explosive mixture farther outbye in the return gate. When the flame reached that area, possibly 100 yards outbye the main ripping, rapid burning would occur, producing strong blast waves in both directions. The flame would then travel with increasing velocity into highly explosive pre-mixed firedamp outbye along the return gate, giving rise to the extreme violence observed at the

junction of the return gate and the Maindy Heading Return. There was evidence of fairly heavy burning but little of violence inbye of the main ripping in the return gate. Flame appeared to have travelled down the face to about its mid-point but the effect of blast here was slight. This suggested that the flame on the face had been mainly an extension of the explosion in the return gate, rather than that the face itself had been excessively fouled with firedamp. That the explosion had virtually died out on the face is shown by the fact that only slight signs of blast but none of burning were found in the intake gate.

61. The volume of return gate and face affected by flame was about 2,000 cubic yards. Any calculation of the quantity of firedamp involved would be subject to a number of uncertainties, but a figure of 1,000 cubic feet of pure methane would not be inconsistent with the flame pattern observed. This quantity of firedamp corresponds with that likely to have been present in the layer found in the course of the experiments to which I have referred earlier. The evidence was that coal-dust had played a very insignificant part in the explosion.

Conclusions.

62. I am satisfied that the evidence given at the Inquiry covered all the relevant aspects. This, together with the professional opinions offered and helpful submissions which were made at the close of the Inquiry, has enabled me to reach firm conclusions on the cause of the explosion and the circumstances leading up to it.

63. Much of the Inquiry turned upon the air bridge over the Maindy Heading Return. Experiments demonstrated that, even when the access holes in the air bridge were covered, air leaked to a marked degree into the Maindy Heading Return. While some of this leakage could have been the result of badly fitting covers to the holes, the probability is that the greater part resulted from the generally poor construction of the air bridge. One can understand that an expedient, such as the access facility in the air bridge, may have been necessary in the early days when the district was being opened up and while arrangements were being made for a properly equipped connection. This was said to be the intention of the management and, although at the outset some work was undertaken, this was not continued. Instead, it seems that reliance was placed on a system whereby the access holes were to be used for the passage of men and materials, but for only short periods of time. In practice, however, the smaller access hole equipped with a ladder for the passage of men seems to have been allowed to stay open, if not for the whole of the time, certainly for the greater part of it. In so far as the larger access hole is concerned, it seems reasonably clear that, prior to the morning of the explosion, it was opened only infrequently and then for periods of no more than an hour and not on every shift. Before the P11 District was encountered, the effect on the face ventilation of leaving the smaller access hole open was probably only marginal, but opening the larger access hole at the same time would have a more marked effect. Even under these conditions, and despite the air bridge leakage, there was still, in my opinion, sufficient air to provide adequate ventilation for the face. But the poor construction of the air bridge and the way in which it was used were examples of deplorably bad pit practice, which should not have been tolerated by anyone having responsibilities for the safe working of the mine.

64. Paradoxically, it is in the excessive quantity of air available to the P26 District that I find the real key to the circumstances of this explosion. In a situation in which the firedamp content of the return air was low and in which the air available was greatly in excess of requirements, the defects in the air bridge and the way in which it was used were accepted as being of little consequence and a sense of complacency in regard to the ventilation seems to have been engendered in everyone concerned. This sense of complacency continued after the P11 District was contacted, even though the effect of the holing was to change quite dramatically the distribution of ventilating pressure throughout the district.

65. With the ladder way open, the quantity of air passing over the air bridge was about 9,000 cubic feet per minute, but, of this, some 3,000 cubic feet per minute was then lost into the P11 workings, leaving 6,000 cubic feet per minute for the P26 face. When both access holes were open, however, only about 4,000 cubic feet of air per minute

passed over the air bridge; with a loss of 3,000 cubic feet per minute into the P11 workings, the quantity of air available for the face was then reduced to no more than about 1,000 cubic feet per minute. I regard this quantity as being totally inadequate for the proper ventilation of the face in any circumstances.

66. Thus, while only one access hole was open, all was seemingly well but, whenever the second access hole was opened, a potentially dangerous situation arose, in that the velocity in the return gate must then have fallen to as low as 20 feet per minute. With a velocity of this order, there was always a distinct possibility of firedamp layering, given that firedamp was being emitted into the roadway. In my opinion, there was just such an emission, and a layer developed whenever the two access holes were open. That layering was never detected is probably explained by the fact that, up to the day of the explosion, the two access holes were open together for only short periods and thus the interruptions in ventilation would have been of short duration; upon the restoration of the normal velocity, as experiments showed, any accumulation of firedamp would be quickly dispersed.

67. Everyone concerned at the colliery regarded the Pentre coal seam and the P26 face in particular as virtually gas free. The management were no doubt fortified in this belief by the fact that the statutory mine air samples taken during normal coal production never showed more than 0·38 per cent of firedamp equivalent to a 'make' of 30 Cubic feet per minute into the face air stream. When coaling was not in progress this was reduced to about ten cubic feet per minute. From measurements taken after the explosion it may be deduced that concentrations of firedamp in the waste were negligible and that there was little increment in the firedamp content of the air for the first 120 yards of the return gate outbye the main ripping. Outbye this point there was, however, an accession of about 20 cubic feet per minute of firedamp. This region of emission was in the vicinity of the pillar from which the face started and hence a place where roof break would be induced as the face moved away. These breaks would extend to seams above and provide a passage for firedamp to migrate from these seams into the P26 Return Gate. This migration of firedamp would depend neither upon the ventilation pressures across the district nor upon the nature of the operations on the face; it would fill any cavities over the arches, but in spilling it out into the roadway it would be readily dispersed if the speed of the ventilation was around 100 feet per minute. At velocities somewhat below 75 feet per minute but in excess of 20 feet per minute, as was shown by experiment the firedamp would not be completely dispersed and would form a layer, the length and depth of which would increase as the velocity decreased. Furthermore because of the rising gradient of the road, the layer would move rapidly uphill against the air stream. The experiments showed that, in two and a quarter hours, a layer such as this could extend as far back as the ripping lip and increase to over four feet so that its lower fringe was below the level of the top of the switches.

68. The evidence clearly established that, on the morning of the explosion, both access holes in the airbridge were open at the time of the explosion and had been in that condition for at least two and a half hours. With such a prolonged interruption in the ventilation of the district, everything points to the likelihood that by 12:55 p.m. that morning a situation very similar to that obtained by experiment had developed and that sufficient firedamp had accumulated in the return gate to sustain the ensuing explosion.

69. The point of ignition was clearly in the gate-end switch controlling the return end plough motor. All the evidence points to the fact that two electricians were trying to locate a fault which had stopped the motor and for this purpose had opened up the switch by withdrawing the ten bolts which held the hinged cover in place. It is reasonable to presume that they were carrying out a sequence of tests employing the not uncommon method of connecting control circuits to earth via a rectifier. This would have the consequential effect of operating the contactor within the gate-end switch, creating an arc of some intensity Such arcing always accompanies the operation of a switch; this is clearly recognised and is safeguarded by locating the switch in a flameproof enclosure. For reasons which come readily to mind, the electricians did not close and bolt the cover of the switch, thereby destroying its flame proofness. Unfortunately this occurred at a time when the atmosphere surrounding and within the switch had, unknown to them, become charged with inflammable gas.

70. For the National Coal Board it was accepted that the switch was the point of ignition and that firedamp had issued from the strata in the length of the return gate at a short distance inbye the top of the drift. It was suggested, however, that this issue commenced less than an hour before the explosion. This I regard as an extremely remote possibility; it is far more likely that the firedamp had been issuing into the return gate from breaks induced since soon after the face started moving away from the solid coal.

General Remarks

Firedamp Determination and Layering.

71. This explosion focuses attention on two closely related subjects, firstly, the emission of firedamp, from a source other than the seam being worked into a face return roadway, as a factor to be taken properly into account in assessing the ventilation situation and, secondly, the propensity for firedamp to form roof layers, particularly where the ventilation velocity is low. The firedamp determination in the general body of the air taken at the statutory sampling point ten yards outbye the P26 face was less than 0·4 per cent when coaling was in progress and was 0·1 per cent when it was not. By reference to this data alone, it is reasonable to presume that the management concluded that there was no real firedamp problem. But in the event, such a conclusion must have been wholly false for, whilst the 'make' inbye of the statutory sampling point was low, about 20 cubic feet per minute of firedamp were being emitted, into the return, well outbye the statutory sampling point. As I have recounted, S.M.R.E. scientists and inspectors demonstrated that this firedamp, because of defective ventilation, formed a layer of dangerous proportions which backed uphill against the sluggish air-current, and eventually led to a disastrous situation.

72. Whenever firedamp emission into a roadway occurs well outbye from the face there is always the possibility of a dangerous situation developing if there is any marked reduction in air speed. The emission into the P26 Return Gate could have been recognised, and evaluated, by a simple determination of the firedamp content in the general body of the air at the outbye end of the return. It seems to me, therefore, that there is much to be said for making it a statutory requirement that firedamp determinations be made at the end of face return roadways as nearly as possible at the same time as the present statutory determination, and this I recommend should be done. With the knowledge of an increase in the firedamp content, it is a relatively easy matter to seek out the point or points of emission and to take such precautions as may be necessary. Pending the making of the statutory provisions, I should like the National Coal Board to arrange administratively for such determinations to be made and recorded.

73. It should be remembered that layers may move against the ventilating current even when the inclination of the roadway is slight. This is being recognised more and more as a phenomenon which is by no means a rare occurrence. The likelihood of layering depends on three factors, namely, the rate of emission of the firedamp, the cross-sectional area of the road and the velocity of the ventilating current.

74. The S.M.R.E. have carried out a great deal of research into layering and have published conclusions, which are, broadly, that the risk of layering can be determined mathematically by reference to the three factors mentioned above. They have also arrived at a formula which, utilising the statutory firedamp determination as the first factor, gives a figure which is an indication of the probability of layering taking place. This figure, termed the "layering index", has been described and discussed in the Establishment's Annual Report for 1963, and in an article entitled 'Firedamp Roof Layers' by S.J. Leach and A. Slack (published in Colliery Engineering, May, 1964).

75. The application of the formula is based on the presumption that, in any given situation, an indication of whether or not a risk of layering exists will hold good both inbye and outbye the measuring point. This is probably quite reasonable in the great majority of cases, but it could well be otherwise in a wholly unusual situation, such as developed in P26 District, where the return roadway emission was independent of the district 'make' and as great as that of the rest of the district, while the ventilation velocity was at times sluggish in the extreme. A more realistic appraisal of the position

could have been derived from a calculation of the layering index using a determination of firedamp content taken at the outbye end of the return roadway in accordance with my recommendation above.

Firedamp Detection and Monitoring.

76. In the course of submissions, reference was made to the shortcomings of the flame safety lamp in the detection of thin layers of firedamp; however, the National Coal Board has proposals for the introduction of lamps of the Garforth type or lamps modified to accept a probe.

77. It was also put to me that there was a need for instruments which would continuously monitor the firedamp situation in a district. I quite agree with this view for this explosion has shown that the time is now overdue for a reappraisal of the methods used in mines today to detect firedamp. I certainly do not envisage the use of instruments which have to be carried in and out of a district every shift. I have more in mind the kind of instrument to which I referred in my recent Annual Report, namely a methanometer designed to operate a suitable alarm system and to isolate automatically the electricity supply into a district. So far as I am aware there is nothing to prevent a further development of this so that a number of such instruments are installed at potentially vulnerable points in a ventilating district and then coupled together to provide continuous monitoring of the firedamp conditions there.

78. I am aware that, apart from the instrumentation of automated faces, research and development is proceeding in this matter; I most earnestly recommend that it be accorded a high degree of priority.

The Testing of Flameproof Apparatus.

79. The front cover plate of the gate-end switch involved in this explosion was secured by ten bolts. To ensure that a flameproof enclosure is in fact flameproof it is essential that all cover bolts are in position and properly tightened whenever the power is applied. Thus electricians wishing to gain access to the interior for any purpose are faced with the prospect every time of removing ten bolts and replacing them before applying power. When repeated adjustments have to be made, this procedure would have to be followed many times.

80. One can, therefore, understand, but not excuse, electricians who are tempted to avoid this tedious process by not always replacing bolts before applying power. But it is imperative that they recognise the danger and do not default in this respect. What can be done to give them practical assistance in this matter is to provide adequate means for testing the operation of the switchgear and suitable instruments for tracing external faults. There may well be an advantage also in the use of gate-end switches having covers which are secured or locked by single bolts and are thus much easier to remove and replace.

81. Many types of gate-end switches are designed with integral testing facilities which enable an electrician to determine whether a fault exists in the control circuits within the switch itself or whether the fault is external to the switch. An alternative device for this purpose is a test plug which simulates an external control circuit and so assists in checking the operation of a switch. In this instance the switch being tested was not equipped with integrated testing facilities but a test plug was available in the district. This, however, was over 400 yards away at the face end of the other gate and one must, I think, recognise that not only was distance a major consideration, but that the plug itself was awkward to carry. In the circumstances, the electricians probably adopted the expedient of using a rectifier, a procedure to be deprecated.

82. 1 consider that, as an immediate measure in places where firedamp is a hazard, existing gate-end switches or banks of such switches not having integral testing facilities should be provided with a test plug. The ultimate must, however, surely be the provision of testing facilities as an integral part of all gate-end switches and I recommend accordingly. Further, so that faults in control circuits external to the switchgear may be more readily traced, I recommend that test instruments designed for this purpose should be developed.

Recommendations

83. I recommend that: (1) there should be a statutory provision requiring firedamp determinations to be made at the end of face return roadways, as nearly as possible at the same time as the present statutory determinations are made;

(2) a high degree of priority be accorded to the development of instruments and systems for the continuous monitoring of firedamp;

(3) in places where firedamp is a hazard, all gate-end switches should have integral testing facilities, but pending this every switch or bank of switches in such places and not so equipped, should be provided with a test plug; and

(4) test instruments designed for tracing faults in control circuits external to switchgear should be developed.

Acknowledgments.

84. I must record my thanks to Mr S. Tapper-Jones, the Town Clerk of Cardiff, for making available the very excellent accommodation for the Inquiry, and to Mr T.G. Morris, the Chief Constable, and his officers for their unstinted help before and during the proceedings. I am grateful to Mr T.I. Hillman, Area Chief Surveyor, and his staff, and to Mr Hillman personally for his assistance at the Inquiry.

My thanks are also due to all those concerned in the investigation prior to the Inquiry; the staff of the National Coal Board, representatives of mining officials and workmen, members of the Safety in Mines Research Establishment, and of H.M. Inspectorate of Mines and Quarries. Particularly, however, I am indebted to the representatives of the interested parties, not only for their courtesy, but for having given me their complete co-operation throughout the Inquiry. In conclusion I should like to acknowledge the valuable assistance rendered by Messrs. A.R.D. Murray and C.J. Lewis-of the Ministry of Power both during the Inquiry and in the preparation of this report.

I have the honour to be, Sir,

Your obedient Servant,

H.S. Stephenson.

Explosion At Tower Colliery, Glamorganshire

Report On the causes of, and circumstances attending,

The explosion which occurred at Tower Colliery, Glamorganshire,

On 12th April 1962

14th September 1962

The Right Honourable Richard wood, MP

Minister of Power

Sir,

1. In accordance with your direction, given under the terms of section 121 of the Mines and Quarries Act, 1954, I beg to submit my report on the causes of, and circumstances attending, the explosion which occurred at Tower Colliery, Glamorganshire, on 12th April 1962, when eight persons were killed, one was fatally injured and nine others sustained serious personal injuries.

2. On 11th May, 1962, Mr T. Alwyn John, HM Coroner for North Glamorgan, sitting with a jury, concluded the holding of an inquest on the bodies of nine persons. A verdict was recorded that all nine had 'died as a result of multiple injuries accidentally received in an explosion in the MC3 road at Tower Colliery'.

3. My investigations showed that the explosion was caused be a severe short circuit to earth in an electric cable in the presence of a body of inflammable gas.

Description Of The Colliery

General.

4. Tower Colliery is in the No.4 Area of the National Coal Board's South Western Division and is situated in the village of Hirwaun some four miles north west of Aberdare. The colliery 'take' is located close to the recognised base of the Lower Coal Measures and is centrally placed along the northern outcrop of the coalfield. Records show that coal was first mined here in the year 1864. The 'take' is traversed by three large faults which naturally divide the mine into three parts. This natural division combined with a scheme of re-organisation and modernisation has resulted in the mine being served by six cross measure drifts from the surface and three vertical shafts. The output of the colliery is some 1,500 tons per day. The number of persons employed underground is 938 and 234 persons are employed on the surface.

5. The ventilation of the mine is produced by two fans. At the No.1 upcast shaft a Sirocco single inlet fan produces 95,000 cubic feet of air per minute at a water gauge of 4·1 inches while at No.4 upcast shaft a similar type of fan produces 180,000 cubic feet of air per minute at a water gauge of 2·8 inches.

6. Safety lamps are used throughout the mine. For general lighting purposes Oldham Wheat W type electric cap lamps are used. Senior officials and deputies use Thomas and Williams Cambrian type No.8 flame lamps which are used as gas detectors by appointed workmen.

7. The coal seams worked during the life of the colliery have been, in descending order, Four-Feet, Six-Feet, Red Vein, Nine-Feet, Bute, Seven-Feet and Five-Feet. At the time of this explosion the Nine-Feet, Seven-Feet and Five-Feet seams were being worked.

8. Among the persons who have been given written instructions for securing the National Coal Board's statutory responsibilities at this mine are:

Mr T. Wright	Area General Manager
Mr P.G. Weekes	Area Production Manager
Mr V. Lewis	Deputy Area Production Manager (operations)
Mr S. Thomas	Deputy Area Production Manager (planning)
Mr T.G. Jones	Group Manager

The colliery manager is Mr T.J. Ryder. There are three undermanagers of whom Mr C.J. Bell was responsible for the affected area.

9. The only area of the mine affected by this explosion was contained within that part known as 'Tower 4' and served by the No.3 Drift and the No.3 New Drift as intake airways and the No.4 upcast shaft. This area was known as the 'G' panel and the seam worked here was the Nine-Feet.

The 'G' Panel

10. 'G' panel was developed following the establishment of a new ventilation circuit of which the No.3 New Drift formed the main intake with a main return by way of a cross measure drivage to the No.4 upcast shaft. From these main airways two levels at 30 yards centres were driven narrow on the strike of the seam to the limit line of working some 850 yards inbye. In this area the Nine-Feet coal seam was found to vary little from 7 feet 6 inches in thickness with a strong clift roof and a hard fireclay floor. The volatile matter content of the coal seam varied between 9·3 and 10·2 per cent.

11. At the time of the explosion there were two working places in the panel. One, to the dip from the levels and worked by a Continuous Miner, is referred to as the 'Miner' heading. This heading was not affected by the explosion. The second working place was developed near to the inbye end of the levels and to the rise. This heading, known as the MC3 heading, was the scene of the explosion.

12. The immediate supervision of the panel was by an overman and a deputy on the morning shift. On the afternoon and night shifts supervision was exercised by deputies with assistance from overmen who also had responsibility for other districts. On each shift there was a shotfirer. A second official with the status of a deputy was also employed in the 'Tower 4' part of the colliery to supervise closely the arrangements for the ventilation of the several narrow drivages.

The MC3 Heading.

13. The MC3 heading had been driven at a rising gradient of 1 in 10·5 in the full thickness of the seam for a distance of 328 feet and was 12 feet wide. The coal was won by shotfiring out of the solid and loaded on to a short scraper chain conveyor by means of a Samson MC3 Loader. The chain conveyor delivered on to a belt conveyor down the heading which in turn delivered on to the main gate belt conveyor in the return level. Coal was worked on each of the three shifts.

14. The support in the heading was by straight H section girders, 6 inches by 5 inches, carried on wood props set at the road sides.

15. All the machinery in the heading was electrically driven. The electrical apparatus supplied from a 300 kVA. 3300/550 volts flameproof transformer in a substation in the 'G' return roadway some 500 yards outbye the MC3 heading. The neutral point of the 550 volts winding was earthed. On the primary side of the transformer there was an oil-immersed circuit breaker which was fitted with time-lagged overload trips set at 50 amperes and an instantaneous earth leakage device connected to a current transformer in the secondary neutral lead and arranged to trip the circuit breaker when a current of 2½ amperes flowed from phase to earth in the 550 volts system.

16. The secondary side of the transformer was connected by means of a short length of 0 15 square inch paper insulated, lead covered, double wire armoured cable to a flameproof air-break section switch in the same substation. This switch was provided with an isolator and a hand operated circuit breaker, and was fitted with thermal overload trips set at 142 amperes, instantaneous short circuit trips arranged to operate at 2,000 amperes and an instantaneous earth leakage device designed to trip when a current of 3½ amperes flowed from phase to earth.

17. The earth leakage devices were designed to trip and lock out mechanically the respective switches on the occurrence of an earth fault on the 550 volts system, and to indicate, by means of a flag visible from outside, that such a fault had occurred. A test button was also provided on each switch so that the correct functioning of the devices could be tested.

18. An 0.04 square inch paper insulated, lead covered, double wire armoured 550 volts feeder cable from the section switch passed inbye along the return roadway to a flameproof gate end switch controlling the 'Miner' heading conveyor. The supply was looped through the busbars of this switch to a cable coupling tee box from which the apparatus in the 'Miner' heading was supplied whilst the cable continued to the MC3 heading. This length of cable was looped through the busbars of a flameproof drill panel, a flameproof gate end switch controlling the auxiliary fan ventilating the MC3 heading, and a flameproof gate end switch controlling the MC3 belt conveyor. Both these switches were situated in the return roadway a few yards from the entrance to the MC3 heading. From the last switch the cable passed up the MC3 heading to two coupled gate end switches placed at a point some 20 yards back from the face of the heading. One of these switches controlled the scraper chain conveyor and the other the MC3 loader. The feeder cable was connected to the inbye end of the busbars of these switches, i.e., it was looped back on itself.

19. The MC3 heading was ventilated by a 16 inches diameter Meco axial flow auxiliary fan forcing air from the intake level through ducting 20 inches diameter. The fan was situated in the connection between the intake and return levels some 12 yards outbye the MC3 heading. The manager had prescribed that a minimum quantity of 2,100 c.f.m. should be delivered at the face.

Events Immediately Before The Explosion

20. On the night shift immediately prior to the explosion coal had been filled normally for the first half of the shift but was interrupted by a mechanical breakdown in the MC3 loader. Because this breakdown could not be repaired without some delay it was decided to complete the shift by shortening the scraper chain conveyor and lengthening the belt conveyor. This work had not been completed at the end of the shift and was carried on during the succeeding morning shift when the normal complement of seven persons in the heading was augmented by two persons from other places in the district. Also in the heading were two fitters working on the MC3 loader, and the ventilation official who was subsequently joined by three electricians. Approaching the heading by way of the return roadway were two representatives of the workmen engaged on inspection duties.

21. The movement of the conveyors made it necessary to move forward the two coupled gate end switches, controlling the scraper chain conveyor and the MC3 loader, and the addition of a new length of cable. Electricians, N. Lewis (Class I), T. Davies (Class II) and an apprentice, M.A. Pearce, were instructed by the electrician in charge of the mine to move the switches and extend the cable. Some difficulty had occurred with a pump in another part of the mine and Lewis had first to attend to that. He ascertained that Davies knew how to proceed with the work to be done in the MC3 heading and instructed Davies and Pearce to go to the heading and start it.

22. Davies arrived in the 'G' panel at about 8:00 a.m. and found the undermanager, C.J. Bell, in the 'Miner' heading. After discussion, Davies cut off the power at the section switch in the substation from both the 'Miner' heading and the MC3 heading; removed the connecting pins in the tee box near the top of the 'Miner' heading and then restored power at the section switch. This action cut off all power to the MC3 heading without interfering with the supply to the 'Miner' heading which was thus able to continue to work. The time was then approximately 9:00 a.m.

23. Davies and Pearce then proceeded to disconnect the gate end switch in the MC3 heading and had almost completed this work when the electrician, Lewis, reached the scene. Leaving Pearce to complete the disconnecting of the switch Lewis and Davies made a test on the length of cable to be installed which, at this time, was lying alongside the main conveyor in the return roadway. Finding the cable to be in satisfactory condition Lewis secured a chain to the end of the cable which was then dragged by a horse for a distance of some 100 yards up the MC3 heading to its new position. This done the gate end switches were dragged into their new position. The time was then a few minutes after 10:00 a.m.

24. The undermanager, Mr Bell, arrived in the heading at this time and was told by the deputy in charge, K. Strong, that the auxiliary fan had been stopped for some 15 minutes; a statement which cannot be reconciled with the fact that the power was cut off at 9:00 am. Some five or six yards back from the face of the heading Bell found a concentration of gas near the roof which he estimated to be about two per cent. He instructed the deputy to send everyone except the electricians back to have food at the bottom of the heading while he remained with the electricians until they completed the connecting up of the switch. This done he came out of the heading with the electricians.

25. Lewis and Davies having first cut off the power at the section switch in the substation restored the connecting pins at the tee box near the top of the 'Miner' heading and went back to the section switch to restore the power to the whole of the 'G' panel. They had not made any test of the re-erected apparatus.

The Explosion And Recovery.

26. Davies was first to reach the section switch and stated that he tried to close the switch but failed because he was 'too quick'. Lewis then closed the switch. He stated that he was watching the ammeter expecting to see the indication of the load of the auxiliary fan starting up when the explosion occurred. At this he put the switch out. The time was now within minutes of 10:30 a.m.

27. The undermanager was in the intake level and went with the overman, who had been in the 'Miner' heading throughout the shift, back to the scene. He telephoned to the surface to inform the manager of the occurrence and then went some distance up the MC3 heading so as to be sure that no persons were there. He described the heading as being too full of dust for anything to be clearly seen. He saw no sign of flame or burning of any description. The normal ventilation of the two levels was only momentarily interrupted.

28. The manager immediately went to the scene and with other officials and workmen gave first aid treatment to the injured and arranged for their conveyance to the surface. The Dinas Rescue station permanent brigade arrived without delay and made an inspection of the heading. Later other brigades assisted in the re-establishment of the ventilation in the heading. For this purpose a separate auxiliary fan was installed and was supplied with current by a separate circuit.

The Investigation

General.
29. The effects of the explosion were confined to the MC3 heading itself and to a short length of the return level outbye of the junction with the heading. There was little or no evidence of flame and indications of violence were apparent only at the junction with the return level and immediately outbye that junction. The degree of violence was not great and the most obvious effects were apparent on the bodies of the victims. Some of the roadside posts were discharged but the natural conditions were such that there was no great pressure on these posts. The explosion was one of gas only; coal dust played no part in it.

Source of Firedamp.
30. An examination of the reports by the deputies showed that they had never found gas in the heading. The ventilation officer of the mine had made determinations of the state of the ventilation in the heading at intervals of approximately one week. The average methane content of the air as reported by him in the five samples taken was 0·46 per cent. However, on the day before the explosion such a determination showed a substantial increase to 0·70 per cent methane in a quantity of 2,985 cubic feet of air per minute delivered at the face of the heading. At this time the volume of air passing the auxiliary fan in the intake was 12,570 feet per minute.

31. The heading had been unventilated for the period of some 90 minutes during which the power had been cut off and the auxiliary fan stopped. In this time the make of gas from the coal sides of the heading and the face was sufficient to produce an explosive concentration. This was confirmed some three days after the explosion when tests were made to determine the rate at which gas accumulated in the heading. Before stopping the auxiliary fan the only gas found was 0.55 per cent close to the roof at the working face. With the fan stopped for 14 minutes a concentration in excess of five per cent was found at the working face and 3 feet 6 inches below the roof. With the fan stopped for 18 minutes a concentration of 1.55 per cent was found at a point 51 feet back from the face and 4 feet 6 inches below the roof.

Means of Ignition.
32. At the time of the explosion there were no persons in the heading and no operations were proceeding there except that power was being applied from a point outbye to the newly extended electrical circuit in the heading. Examination of the electrical apparatus showed that a severe short circuit between all conductors and to earth had occurred in the length of 0·04 square inch P.I.L.C.D.W.A cable newly inserted into the system. A hole, approximately one inch in diameter, had been blown through the cable and the resultant arcing would have been more than sufficient to ignite inflammable gas in the vicinity. The hole in the cable occurred on the inside of the loop formed by bending the cable at the switch, and there is no doubt that the explosion was caused by a short circuit at this point. Further investigations served only to discount any other means of ignition.

General Discussion

The Electrical System.

33. As it was installed the supply of current to the electrical plant in the 'G' panel was controlled from the section switch in the substation and any necessary isolation of the plant in the MC3 heading was done by removing the cable connecting pins in the tee box near the junction of the 'Miner' heading. Such an installation was open to criticism on the grounds that suitable switch-gear should be provided to enable circuits to be isolated safely and recourse to the removal of cable connecting pins should not be necessary. In addition the system was such that any cessation of the supply for any reason meant that the auxiliary fan was stopped. Thus during the progress of any electrical maintenance work or, as in this case, the advancing and re-erection of plant, positive ventilation of the area was impossible.

34. The driving of fully mechanised rapidly advancing narrow headings requires that comparatively short lengths of cable be frequently moved from place to place. The P.I.L.C.D.W.A. type of cable as used in this case is not best suited to this sort of work and better results might be obtained from a pliable wire armoured cable or a P.V.C. insulated cable. But whatever type of cable is used it is obviously undesirable to drag it from place to place by means of a chain fastened round it.

35. It is highly important that insulation and conductance tests of all re-installed cables should be made before the power is restored to the circuit and reliance should not be placed on tests of individual lengths of cable made at some time prior to connection in the circuit. Had such testing been carried out in this case it is possible that the fault would have been discovered.

36. In the investigation the earth leakage devices on both the section switch and the high tension switch were found to be inoperative because of slight defects in the mechanical devices in the switches. Both switches were withdrawn and examined on the surface. It is impossible to say when these mechanical defects originated, but if routine testing of the protective devices had been carried out by the means provided, the defects may well have been revealed and corrected. It is equally impossible to say to what extent the defects contributed to the cause of the explosion. The fault on the cable had to occur before the protective earth leakage devices could operate but the damage to the cable might have been much less severe if the devices had operated correctly and there is a possibility that the ignition might not then have occurred. However in this instance it is probable that the inflammable gas near the point of break in the cable was ignited instantaneously.

37. The standard of maintenance and testing of the electrical plant was not good. The plant in the MC3 heading was not included in the Scheme of Maintenance required to be prescribed by the manager. The reasons advanced for this omission were that the manager had been appointed only some three weeks before the explosion and that during this period the official responsible for the Scheme had been away due to illness. Despite the failure to include the plant in the Scheme there were regular entries in the electricians' log book purporting to show that it had been examined in accordance with the Scheme. The entries in the log book were vague but were said to cover the external examination of all gear including the cables and the checking of gaps in the flameproof covers.

38. The investigation showed quite clearly that the electrical staff in the Tower No.4 mine, consisting as it did of two Class I electricians, one Class II electrician, two persons appointed under Regulation 8(1) (a) of the Mechanics and Electricians Regulations, and two apprentices, was not sufficient properly to maintain the electrical apparatus. Serious and prolonged efforts have been made by the management to obtain the services of more electricians but these have been fruitless. Persons have been trained at this mine only to leave the industry on attaining minimum qualifications. This problem is not peculiar to Tower Colliery and I have no doubt that in framing their mechanisation programmes, the Board are giving careful attention to the availability of qualified technicians.

The Ventilation Of The MC3 Heading

39. The evidence of both officials and workmen was to the effect that with the auxiliary fan running normally the heading was well ventilated and this is generally confirmed by the record of the state of the ventilation. However, the determination made on the day before the explosion revealed a methane content substantially higher than that obtained in the previous week despite a small increase in the volume of air delivered by the auxiliary fan. Nothing could be found to account for this increase in the make of gas except the increased length of the heading with the consequent greater area of coal exposed in the sides. This suggests that the heading was reaching a critical length in respect of the auxiliary ventilation system and emphasises the extreme care necessary in such circumstances. While the actual level of the methane content may not, as in this case, be of legal importance the increment in that content was indicative of trends and demanded careful consideration. The value of statutory sampling of the mine ventilation will be greatly enhanced if these comparisons are made.

40. In spite of the evidence which was given to the effect that when the auxiliary fan stopped, workmen withdrew from the heading and remained out until after the fan restarted, it is a fact that men were working in the heading immediately before the explosion during a period when the fan was not running. Having regard to the system of the power supply to the fan and the fact that in this fast moving heading the conveyors had frequently to be advanced I find it difficult to believe that persons had not worked in the heading on other occasions when it was not positively ventilated.

Conclusions

41. I conclude that the explosion resulted from the ignition of inflammable gas in the MC3 heading. The igniting source was arcing resulting from a short circuit to earth in a newly inserted length of cable serving the electrical equipment in the heading, and occurred on the inside of a loop in the cable where it had been bent back on itself in order to connect it up to the switch in the heading. I think it highly likely that the short circuit was directly due to the insulation of the cable having been weakened as a result of the acute bending to which it had been subjected in making the connection to the switch.

Recommendations

42. I recommend that:
(1) In any system of working requiring the use of an auxiliary fan provision shall be made so that the power supply to the fan may be maintained while any or all of the other plant in that working is shut down.
(2) In any system of working requiring the use of an auxiliary fan arrangements should be made whereby the supply of electricity is automatically cut off from all electrical apparatus in that working place whenever the auxiliary fan is stopped.
(3) In rapidly advancing headings where short lengths of cable have to be inserted frequently, pliable wire armoured cable or P.V.C. insulated cable should be used. Cable should always be transported in such a manner as to ensure that it is not damaged.

Acknowledgements
43. I wish to record my grateful appreciation of all who took part in the investigation of this occurrence on behalf of the National Coal Board, the National Union of Mineworkers, the British Association of Colliery Management, the National Association of Colliery Managers and the National Association of Colliery Overmen, Deputies and Shotfirers; and to express my thanks to Mr J.D. Bowen, Area Surveyor, National Coal Board, who prepared the plan which accompanies this report, and to the members of the clerical staff of the No.4 Area, who provided me with a verbatim record of the evidence given by the witnesses.

I have the honour to be, Sir,
Your obedient Servant,
C. LEIGH
H.M. Divisional Inspector of Mines and Quarries.

Colliery Index